KB076912

이그잼보카 고등 2000

목차

Day 1. .... **3** page
Day 2. .... **7** page
Day 3. .... **11** page
Day 4. .... **15** page
Day 5. .... **19** page
Day 6. .... **23** page
Day 7. .... **27** page
Day 8. .... **31** page
Day 9. .... **35** page
Day 10. .... **39** page
Day 11. .... **43** page
Day 12. .... **47** page
Day 13. .... **51** page
Day 14. .... **55** page
Day 15. .... **59** page
Day 16. .... **63** page
Day 17. .... **67** page
Day 18. .... **71** page
Day 19. .... **75** page
Day 20. .... **79** page
Day 21. .... **83** page
Day 22. .... **87** page
Day 23. .... **91** page
Day 24. .... **95** page
Day 25. .... **99** page
Day 26. .... **103** page
Day 27. .... **107** page
Day 28. .... **111** page
Day 29. .... **115** page
Day 30. .... **119** page
Day 31. .... **123** page
Day 32. .... **127** page
Day 33. .... **131** page
Day 34. .... **135** page
Answers. .... **137** page

Day 1

TEST

번호	영어	한글
1	pending	
2	immense	
3	incur	
4	ruthless	
5	an array of	
6	take hold	
7	frown	
8	be conscious of	
9	take sides	
10	know A by sight	
11	weep	
12	cut from the same cloth	
13	proceed	
14	acrobat	
15	kin	
16	desist	
17	lick	
18	commemorate	
19	belligerent	
20	conserve	

TEST

* 유의어와 반의어에 '0'이 있는 문제는 해당 어휘가 없는 경우이니 그냥 패스하시면 됩니다. 글자수의 (p.)는 '숙어' 표시입니다.

번호	유의어	반의어	영어	글자수
21	be involved in, contribute to	be uninvolved, have no part in	H	11 (p.)
22	enclosure, confinement, closure	Opening, aperture, entrance	E	9
23	Cabin, chalet, bungalow.	Mansion, palace, estate.	C	7
24	liquid, solution, dissolvent	insolvent, bankrupt, indebted	S	7
25	Refurbish, renovate, overhaul.	Neglect, abandon, worsen.	R	11
26	agree, permit, allow	refuse, deny, decline	C	7
27	Permeate, saturate, fill, spread throughout.	Vacate, Leave	P	7
28	hold, grip, seize	release, let go, surrender	G	5
29	Falsehood, misconception, error	Truth, fact, reality	F	7
30	infancy, beginnings, starting point	Tomb, grave, resting place	C	6
31	creep, slink, skulk	reveal, disclose, expose	S	5
32	Attraction, Charm, Appeal	Repel, Deter, Repulse	A	6
33	compassion, sympathy, empathy	scorn, disdain, contempt	P	4
34	Demonstrate, protest, strike	Support, endorse, advocate	P	6
35	chute, descent device, skydiving equipment	Fall, drop, descend	P	9
36	wood, lumber, logs, timberland	metal, concrete, stone	T	6
37	Spade, scoop, dig, excavate, clear	Plant, bury, cover, fill, conceal	S	6
38	recuperate from, bounce back from	succumb to, worsen	R	11 (p.)
39	ponder, contemplate, consider	conceal, hide	R	7
40	When, at the time of, during	Before the age of, after the age of, later in life	A	10 (p.)

TEST

글자수의 (p.)는 '숙어' 표시입니다.

번호	영영	영어	글자수
41	at the highest point or level of	A	13 (p.)
42	To stick or hold together in a unified way.	C	6
43	To take advantage of someone or something for personal gain; to make use of.	E	7
44	The force exerted by magnets and the property of attracting or repelling objects.	M	9
45	move one's head up and down to signal agreement or understanding	N	3
46	to insert or incorporate something into something else	E	5
47	a sharp, pointed, or prickle-covered projection on the stem or branch of a plant; a source of annoyance or difficulty	T	5
48	to contribute or offer something	B	15 (p.)
49	As always or as has been the case consistently.	A	6 (p.)
50	to be related or connected to something	H	21 (p.)
51	Unconventional, peculiar, or deviating from common behavior or norms.	E	9
52	Vulnerable and easily attacked.	P	9
53	To kill in a violent or brutal manner; to greatly impress or amuse.	S	4
54	The use of humor, irony, or exaggeration to criticize or mock people's shortcomings or vices.	S	6
55	To discard or get rid of something; to cast off or release.	S	4
56	To die from suffocation in water, typically by inhaling water into the lungs.	D	5
57	to impose or collect (a tax, fee, or fine)	L	4
58	A religious discourse delivered as part of a church service.	S	6
59	Lacking in density or having very few of something.	S	6
60	A sign or event believed to foreshadow the future, often considered as a divine or supernatural message.	O	4

Day 2

TEST

번호	영어	한글
61	engulf	
62	table of contents	
63	cacography	
64	alchemy	
65	detain	
66	abject	
67	rehabilitate	
68	ponder	
69	dullard	
70	be concerned with	
71	come home to	
72	comprise	
73	come to one's rescue	
74	contiguous	
75	with A in mind	
76	resilience	
77	complement	
78	reluctant	
79	enact	
80	near at hand	

TEST

* 유의어와 반의어에 '0'이 있는 문제는 해당 어휘가 없는 경우이니 그냥 패스하시면 됩니다. 글자수의 (p.)는 '숙어' 표시입니다.

번호	유의어	반의어	영어	글자수
81	Repay, refund, compensate.	Withhold, charge, keep.	R	9
82	Decoration, embellishment, adornment	Eyesore, eyesore, blemish	O	8
83	Rhino, horned mammal.	Herbivore, prey, smaller animal.	R	10
84	Blackmail, coerce, demand	Give willingly, offer, concede	E	6
85	path, trajectory, course	Standstill, halt, stationary	O	5
86	as the crow flies, directly, in a straight line	indirect, circuitous, roundabout	I	11 (p.)
87	inexpensively, affordably	at a high price, expensive	A	11 (p.)
88	arrival, coming, appearance	departure, exit	A	6
89	to some extent, somewhat, in part	absolutely, completely, wholly	I	9 (p.)
90	deviate, wander, diverge	stay on topic, remain focused, stick to the point	D	7
91	deplete, drain, wear out	refresh, rejuvenate, energize	E	7
92	Cannot emphasize enough, cannot stress enough.	Can Only Just, Barely Can	C	9 (p.)
93	submit, turn in, deliver	keep, withhold, retain	H	6 (p.)
94	Obvious, noticeable, prominent	Inconspicuous, hidden, subtle	C	11
95	resentment, bitterness, animosity	Forgiveness, reconciliation, goodwill	G	6
96	sew, needlework, suture	unstitch, rip	S	6
97	raise shoulders, dismiss, disregard	emphasize, accentuate	S	5
98	swing, influence, control	stabilize, balance, steady	S	4
99	Rural, pastoral	Urban, sophisticated	R	6
100	Thrifty, economical, mindful, saving, budget-conscious	Extravagant, wasteful, spendthrift, lavish, impulsive	F	6

TEST

글자수의 (p.)는 '숙어' 표시입니다.

번호	영영	영어	글자수
101	a circular or ring-shaped object; a flexible band often used for games or holding things	H	4
102	Deprived of the power of sensation.	N	4
103	Lacking strength, vigor, or power; weak or frail.	F	6
104	no longer in use or outdated	O	8
105	to duplicate or reproduce; to copy	R	9
106	to originate from or result from something	S	8 (p.)
107	to make changes to A to accommodate or fit with B	A	14 (p.)
108	Using irony or sarcasm to mock or convey contempt.	S	9
109	have as its essential feature	C	9 (p.)
110	Whole and undamaged.	I	6
111	Being widely recognized and celebrated; fame or reputation.	R	6
112	inattentively or thoughtlessly	A	8
113	To poison; excite or stupefy (someone) with alcohol or drugs.	I	10
114	To carry out or complete a task or plan.	F	15 (p.)
115	To forcefully remove a government or ruling authority from power.	O	9
116	Have the opportunity or privilege to do something.	G	7 (p.)
117	by means of this, as a result of this.	H	6
118	to withdraw from an agreement or commitment	B	7 (p.)
119	Worn-out or run-down.	S	6
120	Set or declare someone free from blame, guilt, or responsibility.	A	7

Day 3

TEST

번호	영어	한글
121	dissolve	
122	mature	
123	dense	
124	transcribe	
125	homicide	
126	prehensile	
127	scorn	
128	assure	
129	quantum physics	
130	recant	
131	double back on oneself	
132	in passing	
133	overtake	
134	disparate	
135	rust	
136	quarrel	
137	frigid	
138	behave oneself	
139	fatal	
140	verify	

TEST

* 유의어와 반의어에 '0'이 있는 문제는 해당 어휘가 없는 경우이니 그냥 패스하시면 됩니다. 글자수의 (p.)는 '숙어' 표시입니다.

번호	유의어	반의어	영어	글자수
141	appoint, name, assign	undesignate, unassign, unname	D	9
142	calm, tranquil, peaceful	agitated, turbulent, disturbed	P	6
143	epicurean, connoisseur, foodie	Plain, ordinary, basic	G	7
144	expel, oust, remove	admit, allow, welcome	E	5
145	always, constantly, continuously	never, seldom, rarely	A	10 (p.)
146	education cost, fees, instruction	Non-tuition, non-instruction, lack of teaching	T	7
147	comfort, soothe, reassure	distress, upset, trouble	C	7
148	no matter what, regardless of the expense, by any means necessary	at no cost, at no expense, without any sacrifice	A	10 (p.)
149	be willing to, be ready for, be open to, be available for	be uninterested in, be unwilling for, be disinclined to, reject	B	7 (p.)
150	holy, divine, consecrated	Profane, secular, unholy	S	6
151	eliminate, exterminate, obliterate	preserve, protect, maintain	E	9
152	imitate, copy, emulate	Original, genuine, authentic	M	5
153	inhabit, reside, dwell	Vacate, abandon, leave	O	6
154	clarify, illuminate, explain, reveal	obscure, cloud, confuse	S	11 (p.)
155	shock, impact, shake	smooth, steady, uneventful, tranquil	J	4
156	ground, landscape, topography	Sky, air, atmosphere	T	7
157	contract, catch, suffer from, acquire	recover from, overcome, resist, fight off	C	12 (p.)
158	essential, basic, primary	secondary, nonessential, peripheral	F	11
159	enough, adequate, ample	Insufficient, inadequate, lacking	S	10
160	scorn, contempt, disregard, ignore	respect, admire, esteem, honor	D	7

TEST

글자수의 (p.)는 '숙어' 표시입니다.

번호	영영	영어	글자수
161	to be intelligent and sensible	H	29 (p.)
162	A numerical quantity that represents a part of a whole, often expressed as a ratio of two numbers.	F	8
163	Neat, organized, or orderly.	T	4
164	The state of being in a severely damaged or destroyed condition.	R	4
165	to plan or invent something, especially a clever or original idea	D	6
166	Written or spoken communication or conversation, often of a formal nature.	D	9
167	Extreme suffering or anguish.	D	8
168	A sudden and strong urge or desire to do something; a brief and spontaneous action.	I	7
169	Fluent and persuasive in speaking or writing.	E	8
170	the state of being opposite or contrary	P	8
171	evoking a keen sense of sadness or regret; emotionally moving	P	8
172	To include or integrate something as a part of a larger whole.	I	11
173	The traditional beliefs, stories, customs, and practices of a particular culture or community, often passed down orally.	F	8
174	Involving high expenses or expenditures; expensive.	C	6
175	A significant difference or inequality between two or more things.	D	9
176	to break into many pieces with a violent force; to destroy or damage severely	S	7
177	A show of respect or honor, often in the form of a tribute or acknowledgment.	H	6
178	Unpleasant or offensive.	N	5
179	An event or situation, often of a personal or intimate nature; also, an ongoing activity or matter.	A	6
180	To cause something to change direction, often by turning it aside.	D	7

Day 4

TEST

번호	영어	한글
181	resign	
182	sob	
183	spur	
184	impolite	
185	perish	
186	associate	
187	take in	
188	more of	
189	heterosexual	
190	concentrate A on B	
191	coordinate	
192	trousers	
193	solitary	
194	associate A with B	
195	telling	
196	coffin	
197	brevity	
198	odometer	
199	go about	
200	be content to do	

TEST

* 유의어와 반의어에 '0'이 있는 문제는 해당 어휘가 없는 경우이니 그냥 패스하시면 됩니다. 글자수의 (p.)는 '숙어' 표시입니다.

번호	유의어	반의어	영어	글자수
201	misfortune, accident, bad luck	Fortune, luck, success	M	9
202	sue, prosecute, take to court, challenge legally, bring to trial	agree, reconcile, settle, compromise, harmonize	L	8
203	hypothesize, conjecture, guess	Confirm, ascertain, verify	S	9
204	Excessive, redundant, unnecessary	Essential, necessary, crucial	S	11
205	Chest, breast	Back, spine	B	5
206	Beggar, Destitute, Mendicant	Wealthy, Affluent, Rich	P	6
207	Lose, mislay	Locate, find, keep track of	M	8
208	currently, right now, at this very moment	previously, before, formerly	A	9 (p.)
209	cause, bring about, persuade, prompt	discourage, deter, dissuade	I	6
210	outdated, obsolete, old-fashioned	up-to-date, current, modern	O	9 (p.)
211	attempt, try, endeavor	abstain from, avoid, refrain from	M	6 (p.)
212	evocative, suggestive	non-reminiscent, unreminiscent, forgetful, unmindful	R	11
213	prepare, rally, assemble	Demobilize, deactivate, disband	M	8
214	favored by, popular with	out of favor with, unpopular with	I	11 (p.)
215	pipefitter, plumbing technician	customer, homeowner	P	7
216	necessary, required, essential	optional, unnecessary, dispensable	R	9
217	enjoy, appreciate, have a liking for	dislike, have an aversion to, be repelled by	H	13 (p.)
218	inactive, latent, quiescent, asleep	active, awake, alert	D	7
219	naval officer, commander, fleet admiral	Ordinary seaman, sailor, crew member	A	7
220	grasp, understand, comprehend	lose understanding of, be confused about, misunderstand	G	12 (p.)

TEST

글자수의 (p.)는 '숙어' 표시입니다.

번호	영영	영어	글자수
221	A building used to store or shelter animals, hay, or farm equipment.	B	4
222	To consider or take into account.	M	16 (p.)
223	moderate or mild in terms of climate or behavior.	T	9
224	To twist or alter the shape, meaning, or appearance of something in a misleading or harmful way.	D	7
225	A formal decision or judgment in a legal case; an opinion or conclusion.	V	7
226	Subject to death; deadly or fatal.	M	6
227	To disconnect or separate.	D	8
228	To inquire about someone's well-being or inquire about their condition.	A	8 (p.)
229	by looking quickly or briefly	A	9 (p.)
230	under the most favorable circumstances	A	9 (p.)
231	the invasion and multiplication of harmful microorganisms, such as bacteria or viruses, in the body	I	9
232	throw or hurl something forcefully	F	5
233	Related to heat or temperature.	T	7
234	to spread or disperse widely.	D	7
235	The distance between two corresponding points on a wave.	W	10
236	A regular payment made at fixed intervals, often as part of a retirement plan.	A	7
237	To examine or inspect closely and thoroughly.	S	10
238	Demand payment for a debt.	C	9 (p.)
239	take someone away with strong emotions or excitement.	C	9 (p.)
240	A navigational instrument used to determine direction, often with magnetic properties.	C	7

Day 5

TEST

번호	영어	한글
241	zealot	
242	come into effect	
243	kindle	
244	do one's part in	
245	linger	
246	hand over	
247	accession	
248	arbitrary	
249	substance	
250	at one another	
251	frustrate	
252	cringe	
253	prestige	
254	congregate	
255	allot	
256	determine	
257	inherit from	
258	cluster	
259	react to N	
260	adore	

TEST

* 유의어와 반의어에 '0'이 있는 문제는 해당 어휘가 없는 경우이니 그냥 패스하시면 됩니다. 글자수의 (p.)는 '숙어' 표시입니다.

번호	유의어	반의어	영어	글자수
261	qualified, suitable, entitled	Ineligible, disqualified, unqualified	E	8
262	consecutively, sequentially	all at once, simultaneously	O	15 (p.)
263	Eradicate, eliminate, obliterate, annihilate.	Preserve, protect, save.	W	7 (p.)
264	be engrossed in, be immersed in	be disinterested in, uninterested in	B	12 (p.)
265	Wander, rove, travel, explore, drift	Stay put, settle down, fixate, anchor, remain	R	4
266	Strategy, plan, approach, tactic.	Retreat, withdrawal, surrender.	L	12 (p.)
267	Against, contrary to, at odds with, inconsistent with, incompatible with	In agreement with, consistent with, compatible with, in harmony with	O	10 (p.)
268	not to mention, to say nothing of, far from, much less	include, take into account, consider, factor in	L	8 (p.)
269	grow, nurture, develop	neglect, abandon, ignore	C	9
270	intertwine, connect, mesh	disconnect, separate, unhook	I	9
271	charge, indict, allege	exonerate, vindicate, absolve	A	6
272	Fitness center, workout facility, health club	Sedentary, inactive, lethargic	G	9
273	Gullible, trusting, naïve	Skeptical, cautious, distrustful	C	9
274	simultaneously, suddenly, instantly	Gradually, sequentially, one by one	A	9 (p.)
275	trailblazer, innovator, groundbreaker	Follower, imitator, copycat	P	7
276	empathy, sympathy, kindness	indifference, cruelty	C	10
277	Rebuke, criticize, reprimand	Praise, applaud, commend	R	9
278	leap to a conclusion, rush to a conclusion, hastily conclude	hesitate, deliberate, take time to decide	J	17 (p.)
279	give, award, bestow	Deny, refuse, reject	G	5
280	range, assortment, collection	disorder, disarray, confusion	A	5

TEST

글자수의 (p.)는 '숙어' 표시입니다.

번호	영영	영어	글자수
281	A formal discussion or argument between individuals or groups with differing opinions or viewpoints.	D	6
282	to confirm or validate something once more, often after a certain period of time has passed	R	10
283	to cause a disturbance or stir	M	14 (p.)
284	A religious leader or clergyman.	P	6
285	Extremely beautiful or attractive.	G	8
286	To point out, show, or suggest something; to make known or demonstrate.	I	8
287	In relation to the matter that has just been mentioned.	I	12 (p.)
288	A feeling of sickness with an inclination to vomit.	N	6
289	To live together in the same residence, typically referring to unmarried couples.	C	7
290	The act of repeating or citing someone else's words or the words themselves.	Q	9
291	according to common practice or tradition	B	7 (p.)
292	to harm or cause physical damage to someone or something.	I	6
293	to fall down or suddenly become weak or ineffective	C	8
294	to incorporate an activity into your routine, doing it consistently and repeatedly.	M	18 (p.)
295	energy or vitality	V	5
296	to earnestly request or petition; to plead	E	7
297	The predetermined course of events in one's life; destiny or fortune.	F	4
298	Control or influence something or someone in a skillful or dishonest way.	M	10
299	Belonging to a past era or time; no longer in existence or use.	B	6
300	Upset, interrupt, or bother.	D	7

Day 6

TEST

번호	영어	한글
301	antithesis	
302	traduce	
303	physiology	
304	juvenile	
305	plea	
306	critical	
307	intense	
308	foe	
309	levity	
310	the real deal	
311	crater	
312	untimely	
313	underdog	
314	halt	
315	ruth	
316	march	
317	set an example of	
318	regime	
319	primary	
320	penetrate	

TEST

* 유의어와 반의어에 '0'이 있는 문제는 해당 어휘가 없는 경우이니 그냥 패스하시면 됩니다. 글자수의 (p.)는 '숙어' 표시입니다.

번호	유의어	반의어	영어	글자수
321	Be absorbed in, be immersed in, be captivated by.	Be indifferent to, be disinterested in, ignore.	B	13 (p.)
322	effort, attempt, strive	Abandon, give up, quit	E	8
323	closeness, nearness, adjacency	distance, remoteness, separation	P	9
324	Infeasible, unworkable, unattainable, impossible.	Feasible, Practical	I	13
325	Thorough, complete, all-encompassing, exhaustive.	Limited, Narrow	C	13
326	skill, expertise, mastery	Incompetence, ineptitude, lack of skill	V	5
327	remove, get rid of, eradicate	add, include, retain	E	9
328	Concrete, palpable, real	Abstract, intangible, unreal	T	8
329	regardless, anyhow, nevertheless	in every case, in each instance, in every scenario	I	9 (p.)
330	Praise, applause, recognition.	Criticism, condemnation, disapproval.	A	7
331	fantastic, incredible, extraordinary	Terrible, awful, dreadful	M	9
332	Untruth, lie	Truth, fact	F	9
333	Outdated, antiquated, obsolete, ancient.	Modern, contemporary, current, up-to-date.	A	7
334	be subjected to, be vulnerable to	be protected from, shielded from	B	11 (p.)
335	Grain, cereal, wheat	None (Barley is a specific type of grain)	B	6
336	Ridiculous, absurd, comical, laughable.	Serious, sensible, reasonable.	L	9
337	Proceed with, continue, advance	Halt, stop, regress	T	12 (p.)
338	track, follow, find	erase, remove	T	5
339	at the maximum, no more than, up to	at least, a minimum of, not less than	A	6 (p.)
340	earnings, income, gain	Loss, deficit, financial loss	P	6

TEST

글자수의 (p.)는 '숙어' 표시입니다.

번호	영영	영어	글자수
341	The process of managing and organizing the affairs of an organization or government.	A	14
342	Without beginning or end; existing outside of time; everlasting.	E	7
343	to have established habits, opinions, or routines that are difficult to change	S	13 (p.)
344	having the necessary skills, knowledge, or experience to do	Q	13 (p.)
345	more than half of a total	A	11 (p.)
346	Existing in thought or as an idea, rather than a physical reality; theoretical or conceptual.	A	8
347	be owned by N	B	9 (p.)
348	A change in the genetic material of an organism.	M	8
349	To act as a judge or arbitrator in a dispute.	A	10
350	Begin a course of action, especially one that is important.	E	6
351	come out or become visible after being hidden	E	6
352	On the opposite side of a table.	A	14 (p.)
353	to start successfully	G	15 (p.)
354	to cause someone to feel ashamed or humiliated	M	7
355	A formal assembly of representatives or delegates, often for legislative purposes.	C	8
356	decorate or add beauty to	A	5
357	A small, raised bubble on the skin filled with fluid, typically caused by friction or heat.	B	7
358	A group of letters added to the end of a word to change its meaning or form.	S	6
359	to memorize something thoroughly	B	7 (p.)
360	To undermine or disrupt.	S	8

Day 7

TEST

번호	영어	한글
361	fall into place	
362	far from	
363	be founded on	
364	in pledge	
365	depreciate	
366	withhold	
367	assumedly	
368	carnivore	
369	branch	
370	plight	
371	from above	
372	chances are	
373	boredom	
374	nerve	
375	misery	
376	granule	
377	raze	
378	go for	
379	delicate	
380	overhaul	

TEST

* 유의어와 반의어에 '0'이 있는 문제는 해당 어휘가 없는 경우이니 그냥 패스하시면 됩니다. 글자수의 (p.)는 '숙어' 표시입니다.

번호	유의어	반의어	영어	글자수
381	passionate, intense, blazing	calm, peaceful, placid	F	5
382	link with, associate with	disconnect from, detach from	C	11 (p.)
383	delicate, breakable, frail	sturdy, robust	F	7
384	absolute, complete, total	ambiguous, unclear, uncertain	O	8
385	Nevertheless, nonetheless, despite	Therefore, hence, thus	N	15
386	To the detriment of, sacrificing, costing	Without cost to, at the benefit of	A	14 (p.)
387	help, assist, lend a hand	hinder, obstruct, impede	G	9 (p.)
388	bush, shrubbery, underbrush	tree, sapling, plant	S	5
389	Complaint, grievance, resentment	Satisfaction, contentment, approval	G	9
390	Clear, specific, unambiguous	Ambiguous, unclear, vague	E	8
391	moral sense, ethics, inner voice	Indifference, apathy, unconcern	C	10
392	adhere, stick, hold on	release, let go	C	5
393	Warning, predictive, prophetic	Reassuring, calming, comforting	P	11
394	Criminal, wrongdoer, offender, lawbreaker.	Innocent, law-abiding, righteous.	M	10
395	Compete, vie, struggle	Concede, yield, surrender	C	7
396	bitterness, indignation, grudge	contentment, satisfaction, acceptance	R	10
397	determine, decide, settle	hesitate, waver	R	7
398	investigator, sleuth, private eye	Criminal, wrongdoer, perpetrator	D	9
399	because of, on account of, out of concern for	without fear of, unafraid of, fearless of	F	9 (p.)
400	consecutive, sequential, following	non-successive, isolated, sporadic	S	10

TEST

글자수의 (p.)는 '숙어' 표시입니다.

번호	영영	영어	글자수
401	Departing from the normal or typical.	A	8
402	To remain valid, true, or applicable.	H	8 (p.)
403	A weight suspended from a fixed point that swings back and forth under the influence of gravity.	P	8
404	Next to or adjoining something else; neighboring.	A	8
405	to strengthen or support something, often by adding additional material or support	R	9
406	existing in large numbers; many.	N	8
407	To push or force something with sudden or strong pressure.	T	6
408	To become involved or participate in an activity or conversation.	E	6
409	a connection or junction between two or more things	J	5
410	a condition characterized by difficulty falling asleep or staying asleep, often resulting in inadequate rest	I	8
411	The ability to understand or know something instinctively, without the need for conscious reasoning.	I	9
412	To reveal or disclose something.	L	5 (p.)
413	A person who has been rejected or excluded from a group or society; an outsider.	O	7
414	be successful or win in a competition or situation.	C	12 (p.)
415	A potential source of danger or risk; a perilous situation.	H	6
416	Exact, accurate, and without error.	P	7
417	The act or process of creating awareness and attention to something through various forms of media or promotion.	P	9
418	A mark or indentation made by pressing or stamping.	I	7
419	A feeling of anxiety or unease; to make someone feel uneasy or anxious.	D	8
420	To become progressively worse over time.	D	11

Day 8

TEST

번호	영어	한글
421	attorney	
422	humility	
423	from square one	
424	no more than	
425	malnutrition	
426	once and for all	
427	mediate	
428	exquisite	
429	garb	
430	in partnership with	
431	haste	
432	feast	
433	blush	
434	concur	
435	atypical	
436	stubborn	
437	enormous	
438	at the least	
439	heterodox	
440	notorious	

TEST

* 유의어와 반의어에 '0'이 있는 문제는 해당 어휘가 없는 경우이니 그냥 패스하시면 됩니다. 글자수의 (p.)는 '숙어' 표시입니다.

번호	유의어	반의어	영어	글자수
441	Theoretically, conceptually, in theory	In reality, practically, concretely	I	13 (p.)
442	post facto, retrospectively, after the event	before the fact, pre-emptively, beforehand	A	12 (p.)
443	commensurate with, proportional to	disproportionate to, unrelated to	I	14 (p.)
444	in accordance with, in sync with	in conflict with, discordant with	I	13 (p.)
445	fantastic, incredible, marvelous	Unimpressive, ordinary, unexceptional	F	8
446	empty, clear, purge	fill, stock, replenish	C	8 (p.)
447	Comfort, convenience	Discomfort, inconvenience	A	7
448	incubate, develop, emerge	extinguish, suppress, stifle	H	5
449	repress, quell, inhibit	express, reveal, display	S	8
450	demonstrate, reveal, display	hide, conceal	M	8
451	thankfulness, appreciation, recognition	ingratitude, unthankfulness	G	9
452	good, product, item	luxury, rarity, uniqueness	C	9
453	Charm, captivate, attract	Repel, alienate, discourage	E	6
454	follow, chase, seek	retreat, abandon, surrender	P	6
455	deluge, flood, downpour	Drought, dry spell, aridity	T	7
456	labyrinth, puzzle, confusion	clear path, straightforward route	M	4
457	withstand, tolerate, bear	Surrender, yield, give in	E	6
458	induce, provoke, cause	Prevent, stop, deter	B	7 (p.)
459	Mash, mush, paste	Solid, whole, intact	P	4
460	light up, brighten, elucidate	Darken, obscure, shadow	I	10

TEST

글자수의 (p.)는 '숙어' 표시입니다.

번호	영영	영어	글자수
461	To remove or obtain something, often through a process of separation or concentration.	E	7
462	The failure of a pregnancy, resulting in the loss of the fetus.	M	8
463	A state of lawlessness or absence of government or authority.	M	8
464	upright or standing in position.	E	5
465	Sequentially, with one thing happening right after the previous one.	O	16 (p.)
466	The layer at the back of the eye that contains cells sensitive to light, enabling vision.	R	6
467	to make something a permanent part of something else	I	7
468	a person who is killed or injured in an accident, war, or other disaster	C	8
469	Completely in the power or under the control of someone or something.	A	12 (p.)
470	to move forward slowly by dragging the body along the ground or a surface, typically on hands and knees	C	5
471	the ordinary people; the common people	T	9 (p.)
472	to officially prohibit or forbid something; a formal restriction or prohibition	B	3
473	a source of help or support, especially when there are no other options	R	8
474	A failure or defect in a machine or system.	M	11
475	Capable of existing or working together without conflict; harmonious.	C	10
476	To use offensive or insulting language when addressing someone.	C	9 (p.)
477	Providing additional support or assistance; secondary.	A	9
478	Of little value or importance; insignificant.	T	7
479	The desire or need for a product, service, or resource, often in the marketplace.	D	6
480	Impartial or unbiased; not influenced by personal interest or bias.	D	13

Day 9

TEST

번호	영어	한글
481	enrich	
482	discern	
483	apposite	
484	pungent	
485	inflame	
486	concise	
487	flock	
488	aggressive to N	
489	have an impact on	
490	hostage	
491	listless	
492	liberal	
493	confidential	
494	swarm	
495	captive	
496	denature	
497	sojourn	
498	fungus	
499	goods and services	
500	glaze	

TEST

* 유의어와 반의어에 '0'이 있는 문제는 해당 어휘가 없는 경우이니 그냥 패스하시면 됩니다. 글자수의 (p.)는 '숙어' 표시입니다.

번호	유의어	반의어	영어	글자수
501	sharp, perceptive, observant	indifferent, apathetic, disinterested	K	4
502	Precise, accurate, lifelike, true to reality.	Inaccurate, Unrealistic	E	14 (p.)
503	Greed, avarice, covetousness	Generosity, contentment, selflessness	A	15
504	responsible, accountable, susceptible	immune, resistant	L	6
505	mature, ready, developed	unripe, immature, green	R	4
506	Confused, puzzled, uncertain	Knowledgeable, informed, certain	A	7 (p.)
507	devise, plan, concoct	ruin, destroy, dismantle	C	8
508	impartial, unbiased, uninvolved	Biased, prejudiced, partial	N	7
509	be required to do, be compelled to do, be duty-bound to do	free from obligation, optional, voluntary	B	15 (p.)
510	disconcert, abash, make uncomfortable	Comfort, ease, relieve	E	9
511	like, enjoy, be attached to	dislike, detest, loathe	B	8 (p.)
512	suitable, proper, fitting	inappropriate, unsuitable, unfitting	A	11
513	greet, hail, welcome, acknowledge	insult, offend, disrespect	S	6
514	at the latest, by the latest, no later than	at earliest, at the earliest possible time, at the soonest	A	8 (p.)
515	Delay, postpone, dawdle	Act promptly, prioritize, expedite	P	13
516	centigrade, temperature scale, degree Celsius	Fahrenheit, Kelvin, temperature scale	C	7
517	Surpass, exceed, go beyond	Fall short of, lag behind, be inferior to	T	9
518	sadden, dishearten, demoralize	elevate, uplift, raise	D	7
519	nasalized, nasal passage, nose	oral, non-nasal	N	5
520	condemn, criticize	praise, endorse	D	8

TEST

글자수의 (p.)는 '숙어' 표시입니다.

번호	영영	영어	글자수
521	calm or comfort someone or alleviate their distress	S	6
522	impress or overwhelm with brilliance or splendor.	D	6
523	To recognize and highlight the differences between two or more things.	D	11
524	to mention or allude to something	R	8 (p.)
525	Future generations of people.	P	9
526	careful and considerate in one's speech or actions, so as to avoid causing offense or revealing private information	D	8
527	determined and unwavering in purpose or opinion; characterized by firmness and determination	R	8
528	To obtain entry or permission to use or have something.	G	12 (p.)
529	To recall or reflect upon past events or experiences.	L	10 (p.)
530	To take on a particular role, responsibility, or belief without proof or confirmation.	A	6
531	The state of being open and unrestricted for public use.	P	12 (p.)
532	The methods and practices of teaching and education.	P	8
533	having a great deal of money; wealthy	A	8
534	To have a strong feeling of dislike or contempt for someone or something.	D	7
535	not extreme; reasonable or mild.	M	8
536	To eliminate as a possibility; to exclude.	R	7 (p.)
537	To make someone less angry or hostile by making concessions or soothing gestures.	P	7
538	The practice of maintaining order and control through rules, regulations, or training; also, a branch of knowledge or field of study.	D	10
539	To end a telephone call.	H	6 (p.)
540	To surprise or shock someone suddenly, often causing a quick reaction.	S	7

Day 10

TEST

번호	영어	한글
541	mob	
542	ultraviolet	
543	aggrandize	
544	as a matter of fact	
545	compact	
546	facile	
547	forbid	
548	overlook	
549	mingle	
550	dismay	
551	transfuse	
552	factual	
553	reckless	
554	affirm	
555	occur to N	
556	plunge	
557	aggregate	
558	disparage	
559	tactile	
560	fierce	

TEST

* 유의어와 반의어에 '0'이 있는 문제는 해당 어휘가 없는 경우이니 그냥 패스하시면 됩니다. 글자수의 (p.)는 '숙어' 표시입니다.

번호	유의어	반의어	영어	글자수
561	exhaust, fatigue, tire	Refresh, rejuvenate, revive	W	7 (p.)
562	watch, view, witness	ignore, disregard, neglect	O	7
563	ceremony, tradition, custom	Non-ritual, absence of ceremony, lack of tradition	R	6
564	hairless, barren, bald-headed	hairy, furry, well-covered	B	4
565	Beast, Animal, Savage	Human, Civilized, Gentle	B	5
566	regarding, concerning, with respect to	unrelated to, disconnected from, unconnected to	A	4 (p.)
567	control, overpower, rule	submit, yield	D	8
568	Warn, reprimand, scold.	Praise, commend, laud.	A	8
569	forecast, prediction, diagnosis, outlook	uncertainty, unpredictability, ambiguity	P	9
570	vanity, arrogance, egotism	humility, modesty, selflessness	C	7
571	resemble, inherit traits from	differ from, deviate from	T	9 (p.)
572	Walk, amble, saunter.	Rush, sprint, hasten.	S	6
573	Identify, specify, define	Vague, generalize, uncertain	P	7 (p.)
574	courteous, polite, kind	discourteous, impolite, rude	G	8
575	notice, discern, detect	overlook, miss	P	8
576	green, kale, coleslaw	0	C	7
577	pause, break, intermission, interval	continuation, progression, sequence, unbroken flow	I	9
578	expand, inflate, enlarge	Shrink, contract, decrease	S	5
579	make laws, enact legislation, pass laws	repeal, abolish, annul	L	9
580	burst in, invade, rush in, storm	retreat, withdraw, recede	I	6

TEST

글자수의 (p.)는 '숙어' 표시입니다.

번호	영영	영어	글자수
581	have control or understanding of	H	13 (p.)
582	Information or news spread among people.	W	13 (p.)
583	To weaken or erode the foundation, support, or authority of something, often secretly or subtly.	U	9
584	to become rotten or spoiled, to explode or detonate	G	5 (p.)
585	go to a particular place.	M	14 (p.)
586	a blood vessel that carries blood away from the heart	A	6
587	Sufficient or satisfactory in quality or quantity to meet a particular need or purpose.	A	8
588	To recruit or enroll someone, typically into a cause, organization, or military service.	E	6
589	a small stream	R	7
590	put a plan, decision, or system into effect	I	9
591	A branch of mathematics that deals with the properties and relationships of points, lines, angles, surfaces, and solids.	G	8
592	to scatter or spread out	D	8
593	The ability or right to make one's own decisions and govern oneself.	A	8
594	Providing help or assistance.	O	9 (p.)
595	remove the outer layer of something, such as fruit or skin	P	4
596	Reject or decline something; say no to an offer or request.	R	6
597	To move or handle something roughly or in a disorderly manner.	T	9 (p.)
598	to begin a journey or a task with a particular aim or purpose	S	6 (p.)
599	give out or share something among a group	D	10
600	Feeling or expressing anger or outrage at something unjust or wrong.	I	9

Day 11

TEST

번호	영어	한글
601	at the heart of	
602	at one's disposal	
603	be accustomed to N	
604	creed	
605	transition	
606	in case of	
607	intricate	
608	riverine	
609	ethnic	
610	esteem	
611	interpret	
612	comet	
613	attract A to B	
614	compost	
615	etymology	
616	incubus	
617	limp	
618	at a 형 pace	
619	to the contrary	
620	antagonist	

TEST

* 유의어와 반의어에 '0'이 있는 문제는 해당 어휘가 없는 경우이니 그냥 패스하시면 됩니다. 글자수의 (p.)는 '숙어' 표시입니다.

번호	유의어	반의어	영어	글자수
621	genetics, inheritance, genetic traits	Environment, acquired traits	H	8
622	disadvantage, drawback, fault	Merit, advantage, benefit	D	7
623	Relieve, ease, mitigate	Aggravate, intensify, worsen	A	9
624	surpass, outperform, excel	Underperform, fall short, do worse	O	5
625	spot, blemish, discolor	clean, purify	S	5
626	data, numbers, figures	Anecdotes, individual cases, singular data	S	10
627	Mislead, trick, cheat	Inform, clarify, reveal	D	7
628	inhale deeply, take a deep breath	exhale, breathe out	D	15 (p.)
629	repair, renew, revive	Ruin, damage, destroy	R	7
630	reference book, compendium, reference work	Ignorance, unawareness, lack of knowledge	E	12
631	breathe in, respire, inspire	exhale, breathe out	I	6
632	outlaw, renegade, bandit	law-abiding citizen, civilian	D	9
633	lounge, sitting room, salon	kitchen, bedroom, outdoors	P	6
634	intentional, calculated, planned	accidental, unintentional, inadvertent	D	10
635	in line with, compatible with, congruent with	conflicting with, contradictory to, incompatible with	C	14 (p.)
636	nameless, unidentified, unknown	Named, identified, known	A	9
637	Appeal, attract	Repel, discourage	G	6 (p.)
638	minimal, inadequate, insufficient	Abundant, plentiful, ample	S	5
639	examination, inspection, review	ignore, neglect, overlook	A	5
640	supporter, sponsor, benefactor	Critic, opponent, adversary	P	6

TEST

글자수의 (p.)는 '숙어' 표시입니다.

번호	영영	영어	글자수
641	Unclear or not clearly defined; lacking detail or precision.	V	5
642	A sudden attack or assault, typically by a military force or law enforcement.	R	4
643	press or squeeze something together	C	8
644	The act of looking back on or reviewing past events or situations.	R	10
645	A belief or practice resulting from ignorance or fear of the unknown, often with no scientific or logical basis.	S	12
646	explain or justify	A	10 (p.)
647	To harass or torment.	H	5
648	according to the law or legally	B	5 (p.)
649	to make something smaller or decrease in size, quantity, or intensity.	R	6
650	to study intensively or rigorously	H	11 (p.)
651	An organism or cell produced asexually that is genetically identical to its parent.	C	5
652	standing out or noticeable; widely recognized or well-known	P	9
653	To regard with disgust or hatred.	A	5
654	In accordance with the law or accepted rules; valid and legal.	L	10
655	to agree or comply with something	G	11 (p.)
656	to prepare or strengthen oneself for something difficult or unpleasant	B	5
657	To forgive someone for a crime or offense.	P	6
658	promptly or punctually	I	16 (p.)
659	over an extended period of time; eventually	I	12 (p.)
660	The scientific study of humanity, including its origins, behavior, and cultures.	A	12

Day 12

TEST

번호	영어	한글
661	in a split second	
662	marvel	
663	take stock	
664	irrational	
665	by no means	
666	punctuate	
667	hinder	
668	hold together	
669	accord	
670	by way of	
671	rodent	
672	phase in	
673	hygiene	
674	get the message	
675	fluctuate	
676	decry	
677	ail	
678	asterisk	
679	embryo	
680	extinct	

TEST

* 유의어와 반의어에 '0'이 있는 문제는 해당 어휘가 없는 경우이니 그냥 패스하시면 됩니다. 글자수의 (p.)는 '숙어' 표시입니다.

번호	유의어	반의어	영어	글자수
681	disaster, calamity, tragedy	Success, achievement, triumph	C	11
682	elevate, glorify, uplift	humble, degrade, lower	E	5
683	Classic, old-fashioned, antique, retro, timeless	Modern, contemporary, new, trendy, current	V	7
684	To some extent, partially	Completely, fully	A	13 (p.)
685	weaken, thin	concentrate, strengthen	D	6
686	Withdraw, extract, remove	Insert, put in, stay in	P	7 (p.)
687	chaos, confusion, disarray	order, organization, arrangement	D	8
688	Birth, native, original	Postnatal, acquired, non-native	N	5
689	connection, interaction, linkage	disconnect, separate	I	9
690	happen, occur	cease, stop	C	9 (p.)
691	precision, correctness, exactness	inaccuracy, imprecision, error	A	8
692	Modest, unpretentious, meek, self-deprecating, down-to-earth	Arrogant, pretentious, boastful, self-important, egotistical	H	6
693	heavenly, godly, sacred	Human, earthly, mortal	D	6
694	achieve, reach, accomplish	Lose, fail, surrender	A	6
695	Hands-on, practical, interactive.	Theoretical, theoretical, uninvolved.	H	7
696	considering, taking into account, in light of, given	disregarding, ignoring, neglecting	I	8 (p.)
697	Serve as, function as, play the role of	Cease to be, stop being	A	5 (p.)
698	Concerning, regarding, in relation to	Irrelevant to, unrelated to, regardless of	W	12 (p.)
699	compare, equate, analogize	Differentiate, distinguish, contrast	L	5
700	Discourage, dishearten	Encourage, uplift	D	6

TEST

글자수의 (p.)는 '숙어' 표시입니다.

번호	영영	영어	글자수
701	The main structural part of a plant that supports leaves, flowers, and fruit.	S	5
702	an object surviving from an earlier time, especially one of historical or sentimental interest	R	5
703	to take away or deny someone something that they need or desire	D	11 (p.)
704	bestow or confer B upon A as a mark of respect	H	12 (p.)
705	grasp or cling to something	H	6 (p.)
706	to become disheartened or lose confidence	D	7
707	to make fun of someone in a playful way	T	5
708	to restrain or control something, typically an undesirable behavior.	C	4
709	An excessive amount of worry or bother about something unimportant.	F	4
710	the easing of hostility or strained relations, especially between countries	D	7
711	at the present time, by this point	B	5 (p.)
712	A large number or multitude of people or things; a crowd.	M	9
713	superficially; appearing to be true but not necessarily so	O	12 (p.)
714	Extending in the same direction and always equidistant from each other, never meeting.	P	8
715	to the extent or degree that	I	9 (p.)
716	circumvent or avoid something	G	9 (p.)
717	measure the depth of (a body of water)	P	5
718	take advantage of an opportunity	C	12 (p.)
719	A climbing or trailing plant that produces grapes or other fruits.	V	4
720	To combine or merge things into a unified whole.	C	11

Day 13

TEST

번호	영어	한글
721	vinegar	
722	reservoir	
723	abandon	
724	repute	
725	enroll	
726	repress	
727	humid	
728	restrain	
729	sift	
730	carton	
731	surname	
732	at all cost	
733	neural	
734	ballot	
735	in the mood for	
736	neglect	
737	defiance	
738	rear	
739	accumulate	
740	reparation	

TEST

* 유의어와 반의어에 '0'이 있는 문제는 해당 어휘가 없는 경우이니 그냥 패스하시면 됩니다. 글자수의 (p.)는 '숙어' 표시입니다.

번호	유의어	반의어	영어	글자수
741	at one's leisure, when it suits one, whenever one wishes	at a disadvantage, inconveniently, disadvantageously	A	18 (p.)
742	pretend, feign, dissemble	reveal, expose, unveil	D	11
743	spend, use up, consume	Save, hoard, conserve	E	6
744	Rebuff, Reject, Drive away	Attract, Welcome, Accept	R	7
745	Likewise, Similarly, Also	Conversely, On the Contrary, In Contras	B	14 (p.)
746	wild, untamed, ferocious, brutal, fierce	civilized, gentle, tame, domesticated, cultured	S	6
747	release, dismiss, fire	Load, fill, charge	D	9
748	harsh, intense, extreme	Mild, gentle, lenient	S	6
749	Reside, live, inhabit, lodge, remain, sojourn	Depart, vacate, leave	D	5
750	in discussion with, in collaboration with, in coordination with	independently of, unilaterally, without consulting	I	18 (p.)
751	Base, stand, foundation.	Bottom, baseless, ground-level.	P	8
752	ordinary, routine, commonplace	extraordinary, exceptional, remarkable	M	7
753	diverge, stray, veer	Conform, comply, adhere	D	7
754	shooting star, meteoroid, celestial body	stationary object, immovable, fixed	M	6
755	Fleeting, temporary, brief	Permanent, lasting, enduring	T	9
756	deep, intense, significant	shallow, superficial, trivial	P	8
757	Tropical, Equatorial, Torrid	Polar, Arctic, Frigid	T	6
758	ask, query, question	Ignore, neglect, disregard	I	7
759	strive, endeavor, exert	ease, breeze, cakewalk	S	8
760	Imply, suggest, indicate	Denote, specify, state explicitly	C	7

TEST

글자수의 (p.)는 '숙어' 표시입니다.

번호	영영	영어	글자수
761	Capable of being stored without refrigeration for an extended period.	S	12
762	Highly skilled or proficient in a particular activity or field.	A	5
763	Renovate or decorate.	D	5 (p.)
764	Something passed down from a previous generation; a bequest or inheritance.	L	6
765	Revoke or annul (a law or congressional act).	R	6
766	To submit or hand over something, often a task or assignment.	T	6 (p.)
767	To claim or assert without providing proof or evidence.	A	6
768	used to indicate that a word or phrase is being used in a figurative or metaphorical sense	A	8 (p.)
769	A group of mammals that includes humans, apes, and monkeys.	P	7
770	to support, uphold, or maintain something, often over an extended period of time	S	7
771	A person with very low intelligence.	M	5
772	to gather or collect a large amount of something	A	5
773	Being alert, attentive, or vigilant, often to guard against danger.	W	8
774	To choose not to participate in an activity or event.	S	6 (p.)
775	To move quietly or stealthily over a surface.	C	9 (p.)
776	Severe mental or physical pain or suffering.	A	7
777	to persuade or make someone believe or accept something by providing reasons or evidence	C	8
778	to take into account or consider something	F	8 (p.)
779	to smile broadly, often with the teeth showing	G	4
780	a state of strong opposition, animosity, or antagonism towards someone or something	H	9

Day 14

TEST

번호	영어	한글
781	come of age	
782	hierarchy	
783	extrude	
784	mortgage	
785	adolescent	
786	stand out	
787	timescale	
788	on the whole	
789	call A in question	
790	linguistic	
791	misrepresent	
792	dogma	
793	incriminate	
794	pin back	
795	blunt	
796	expedient	
797	lose the day	
798	throne	
799	cruel	
800	reproach	

TEST

* 유의어와 반의어에 '0'이 있는 문제는 해당 어휘가 없는 경우이니 그냥 패스하시면 됩니다. 글자수의 (p.)는 '숙어' 표시입니다.

번호	유의어	반의어	영어	글자수
801	Remove, eject, oust	Secure, fasten, fix in place	D	8
802	Precede, precede in time, come before.	Postdate, follow, come after.	A	8
803	element, part, ingredient	Whole, entirety, complete entity	C	9
804	with the opportunity to, with entry to	without access to, deprived of access to	W	12 (p.)
805	Sleepwalking, noctambulism.	Wakefulness, alertness.	S	12
806	Reject, disown	Embrace, accept	R	8
807	shorten, condense, truncate	Elongate, extend, expand	A	10
808	region, district, administrative division	City, municipality, metropolis	C	6
809	discord, disagreement, conflict, disharmony	harmony, agreement, concord	D	10
810	dictator, autocrat, oppressor	Benevolent ruler, just leader, fair monarch	T	6
811	emphasize, highlight, stress	de-emphasize, downplay, minimize	A	10
812	discover, dig up, excavate	bury, conceal	U	7
813	gardening, cultivation, horticulture	Non-gardening, non-agricultural, urban	H	13
814	viewpoint, perspective, position	Non-standpoint, disregard, neglect	S	10
815	Contradiction, paradox, conflict	Harmony, agreement, consistency	A	8
816	offering, ritual, surrender	Preserve, keep, retain	S	9
817	foreign affairs, international relations, statecraft	Hostility, conflict, antagonism	D	9
818	reverse, flip, turn upside down	Retain, keep, maintain	I	6
819	eliminate, abolish, eradicate	keep, maintain, retain	D	10 (p.)
820	lethal, fatal, mortal	harmless, nonlethal	D	6

TEST

글자수의 (p.)는 '숙어' 표시입니다.

번호	영영	영어	글자수
821	to allow or grant permission for something.	P	6
822	handle, manage, or cope with	D	8 (p.)
823	A diplomatic mission or official residence of an ambassador in a foreign country.	E	7
824	the way someone responds to something	R	11 (p.)
825	detailed, complex, or intricate	E	9
826	A balanced and harmonious arrangement of parts or elements on either side of a central axis.	S	8
827	To understand something fully.	C	10
828	To remember or recall something from the past.	R	9
829	apart from; with the exclusion of	E	9 (p.)
830	A group of stars forming a recognizable pattern in the sky.	C	13
831	Rigid or not easily bent; also used informally to describe a person who is formal or lacking in flexibility.	S	5
832	To think or talk about something at length.	D	7 (p.)
833	to attack someone suddenly and unexpectedly, usually when they are not expecting it	A	6
834	push back or drive away with force.	R	5
835	By a very small margin.	B	16 (p.)
836	to disagree with an opinion or decision	D	7
837	To quote or mention as evidence or an example in support of an argument or statement.	C	4
838	Minimize the significance or importance of something.	D	8
839	A written or spoken explanation or analysis of an event, situation, or piece of work.	C	10
840	A humorous or euphemistic way of referring to the arrival of a new baby.	A	18 (p.)

Day 15

TEST

번호	영어	한글
841	necessitous	
842	dreadful	
843	stance	
844	virtuosic	
845	be subject to N	
846	villain	
847	commotion	
848	hardwire	
849	imperil	
850	scheme	
851	bellicose	
852	surplus	
853	patent	
854	put a strain on	
855	bribe	
856	strive for	
857	at pleasure	
858	reposit	
859	disrupt	
860	malice	

TEST

* 유의어와 반의어에 '0'이 있는 문제는 해당 어휘가 없는 경우이니 그냥 패스하시면 됩니다. 글자수의 (p.)는 '숙어' 표시입니다.

번호	유의어	반의어	영어	글자수
861	Elaborate, elucidate, explain	Confuse, obscure, complicate	C	7
862	thrive, prosper, blossom	decline, wither, wilt	F	8
863	Grant, financial aid, assistance, support, handout	Tax, burden, cost, fee, expense	S	7
864	Consult, Discuss, Deliberate with	Ignore, Disregard, Exclude from discussion	C	10 (p.)
865	suggest, insinuate, indicate	deny, contradict	I	5
866	innocent, gullible, inexperienced	sophisticated, worldly, experienced	N	5
867	Explore, embark on, delve into	Avoid, retreat from, shun	V	11 (p.)
868	Clothing, attire, garments, dress.	Nude, undress, uncover, strip.	A	7
869	jam, traffic, crowd, overcrowding	clear, free, unobstructed, vacant	C	10
870	Decomposition, Rot, Deterioration	Growth, Flourishing, Preservation	D	5
871	put, place, lay down	Withdrawal, removal, taking away	D	7
872	Attribute, Ascribe, Credit	Absolve, Exonerate, Disclaim	I	6
873	tall grass, marsh plant, cane	Hard, firm, rigid	R	4
874	distribute, assign, allot	withhold, retain, keep	A	8
875	accumulate, hoard, store	Deplete, use up, exhaust	S	9
876	behavior, demeanor, performance	misbehave, behave badly, transgress	C	7
877	Comfortable, familiar, adept	Uncomfortable, unfamiliar, inept	A	6 (p.)
878	alleviate, ease, mitigate	intensify, exacerbate	R	7
879	polite, respectful, considerate	rude, impolite	C	9
880	halt A, stop A, cease A	start A, initiate A, begin A	B	13 (p.)

TEST

글자수의 (p.)는 '숙어' 표시입니다.

번호	영영	영어	글자수
881	The sport or practice of using a bow to shoot arrows at a target.	A	7
882	A sharp or witty reply in response to a remark or criticism.	R	6
883	spend more money than one earns	L	21 (p.)
884	The beginning or start of something; the initial stage.	O	6
885	Incorrect or improper use of something.	M	6
886	A respiratory condition characterized by difficulty in breathing, wheezing, and coughing.	A	6
887	a group or collection of things	A	8 (p.)
888	distant or separated from	A	8 (p.)
889	relating to children's medical care	P	9
890	An inherent mental or physical power; an ability or aptitude.	F	7
891	A comparison between two things for explanation.	A	7
892	force or compel B to accept A	I	10 (p.)
893	to provide help or support to someone in need	S	6
894	to treat with unjust or cruel exercise of authority or power; to burden or weigh down heavily	O	7
895	be published or become known	C	7 (p.)
896	to come into a place or situation without being invited or wanted	I	7
897	to hope for good luck or success	C	17 (p.)
898	To recover something lost.	R	8
899	To run short tasks or chores outside the home.	G	11 (p.)
900	A fundamental or basic law that establishes the framework and principles of a government or organization.	C	12

Day 16

TEST

번호	영어	한글
901	furnish	
902	dwindle	
903	hitch	
904	famine	
905	collude	
906	herbivore	
907	damaging to N	
908	evacuate	
909	chop up	
910	fission	
911	to that end	
912	convoke	
913	reconcile	
914	charity	
915	surveillance	
916	remark	
917	reside	
918	go through	
919	come up with	
920	transmit	

TEST

* 유의어와 반의어에 '0'이 있는 문제는 해당 어휘가 없는 경우이니 그냥 패스하시면 됩니다. 글자수의 (p.)는 '숙어' 표시입니다.

번호	유의어	반의어	영어	글자수
921	imagine, envision, think up	forget, ignore, disbelieve	C	8
922	forbid, ban, disallow	permit, allow	P	8
923	cherished, adored, dear	despised, detested, loathed	B	7
924	according to one, from one's perspective, in one's view	objectively, factually, empirically	I	14 (p.)
925	terminate, cancel, cease	continue, proceed, persist	A	5
926	transport, shuttle, boat	Stay, remain, abide	F	5
927	sample, example, representative	Entirety, whole, complete entity	S	8
928	aroma, fragrance, smell	stench, odor	S	5
929	Illusion, hallucination, apparition	Reality, actuality, truth	M	6
930	Nevertheless, nonetheless, still	Different, distinct, unique	A	10 (p.)
931	Terminate, Dismiss, Suspend	Retain, Keep, Continue employment	L	6 (p.)
932	conquer, overcome	surrender, yield	S	6
933	fate, destiny, catastrophe	salvation, success, prosperity	D	4
934	noteworthy, remarkable, prominent	Insignificant, unimportant, ordinary	N	7
935	Achievable, possible, viable	Impractical, unattainable, unrealistic	F	8
936	mediate, interfere, meddle	Abstain, refrain, stay out	I	9
937	Shine, brilliance, radiance	Dullness, tarnish, dimness	L	6
938	impress, amaze, astound	disappoint, underwhelm, bore	B	8 (p.)
939	Religious studies, divinity, philosophy of religion	Atheism, secularism	T	8
940	mix up A and B, mistake A for B	differentiate A from B, distinguish A and B	C	13 (p.)

TEST

글자수의 (p.)는 '숙어' 표시입니다.

번호	영영	영어	글자수
941	State of being well-liked or widely admired.	P	10
942	To overcome or prevail over an opponent or obstacle; to win a victory.	D	6
943	Not in harmony or not working correctly.	O	9 (p.)
944	at some point in the past	A	9 (p.)
945	from one perspective or viewpoint	O	9 (p.)
946	a feeling of deep sadness or sorrow.	M	10
947	A vertical structural support, or a regular feature in a newspaper or magazine presenting information or opinions.	C	6
948	to be useful or convenient	C	11 (p.)
949	to make something impure or polluted by introducing harmful or undesirable substances; to taint or pollute	C	11
950	discounted by fifty percent	H	7 (p.)
951	to make something known or visible; to disclose.	R	6
952	To strike someone on the buttocks as a form of punishment.	S	5
953	To request or ask for something, often in a formal manner.	S	7
954	excellent; of the highest quality	S	6
955	to attract or entice someone or something to move or go in a particular direction; to tempt or allure	L	4
956	To face a difficult situation or challenge directly.	C	8
957	A place of safety.	R	6
958	an exclamation used to encourage or urge someone to do something	C	6 (p.)
959	A young bovine animal, especially a domestic cow or bull.	C	4
960	contrary or contrary to the nature or characteristics of N	O	11 (p.)

Day 17

TEST

번호	영어	한글
961	synthetic	
962	cavity	
963	carefree	
964	polytheism	
965	cut down on	
966	iron out	
967	solidify	
968	prudent	
969	seizure	
970	craft	
971	unison	
972	domineer	
973	by means of	
974	interwine	
975	tribute	
976	recede	
977	straightforward	
978	preside	
979	intrigue	
980	acne	

TEST

* 유의어와 반의어에 '0'이 있는 문제는 해당 어휘가 없는 경우이니 그냥 패스하시면 됩니다. 글자수의 (p.)는 '숙어' 표시입니다.

번호	유의어	반의어	영어	글자수
981	snake, lizard	mammal, bird	R	7
982	Hero, main character, lead role.	Antagonist, villain, antagonist.	P	11
983	explode, rage, become furious	remain calm, stay composed	H	13 (p.)
984	Profane, violate, defile	Reverence, sanctify, respect	D	9
985	estimated, rough, close	Precise, exact, accurate	A	11
986	obstruct, hinder, impede	Assist, facilitate, support	B	10 (p.)
987	authentic, real, true	Fake, counterfeit, phony	G	7
988	Clothing, attire, apparel	Nakedness, undress	G	7
989	Renounce, relinquish, resign.	Ascend, inherit, claim.	A	8
990	strengthen, reinforce, secure	weaken, debilitate, enfeeble	F	7
991	filament, string, strand	tangle, knot	T	6
992	0	related to the throat or faucal region (no direct antonyms)	F	6
993	gardening skill, plant expertise	brown thumb, gardening ineptitude	G	10 (p.)
994	Proceed, continue, advance.	Halt, pause, stop.	G	9 (p.)
995	indecent, lewd, vulgar, offensive, explicit	decent, modest, proper, respectable, tasteful	O	7
996	adorn, decorate, beautify, enhance	simplify, strip, diminish, reduce	E	9
997	Rule, sovereignty, dominance	Submission, defeat, overthrow	R	5
998	encroach, intrude, violate, transgress	obey, respect, adhere	T	8
999	Trade, exchange, swap, negotiate.	Buy, sell, purchase, trade.	B	6
1000	Wander, roam	Stay, remain	S	5

TEST

글자수의 (p.)는 '숙어' 표시입니다.

번호	영영	영어	글자수
1001	To bend or change the direction of light or sound waves as they pass through a medium.	R	7
1002	to cause or make something happen	B	10 (p.)
1003	To give evidence or speak under oath in a court of law.	T	7
1004	To suspend or postpone a meeting, legal case, or event to a future time.	A	7
1005	To die or cause someone to die by depriving them of air or oxygen.	S	9
1006	Conceal or disguise one's true feelings or beliefs.	D	9
1007	A period of temporary economic decline.	R	9
1008	To slander or criticize someone's reputation.	A	7
1009	To improvise or speak without preparation.	E	11
1010	have a valid or reasonable argument	H	10 (p.)
1011	Happening at an appropriate or well-chosen moment; punctual.	T	6
1012	A temporary respite or withdrawal from an activity or pursuit.	R	6
1013	indifferent or unresponsive to N	C	7 (p.)
1014	a period of ten years	D	6
1015	A way to express a multiplication by a certain number.	B	11 (p.)
1016	Plants in general, especially the plants that grow in a specific area or habitat.	V	10
1017	Unfamiliar phrase; possibly a variation of "what it's like."	W	9 (p.)
1018	To suffer or die from lack of food; to go without eating for an extended period.	S	6
1019	A feeling of hopelessness.	D	7
1020	relating to or concerned with human welfare	H	12

Day 18

TEST

번호	영어	한글
1021	elucidate	
1022	fulfill	
1023	verbal	
1024	apparent	
1025	given that	
1026	sumptuous	
1027	antidote	
1028	paralyze	
1029	be equal to N	
1030	condemn	
1031	make my day	
1032	pedestrian	
1033	rip off	
1034	have a problem with	
1035	hibernate	
1036	infant	
1037	incidence	
1038	transparent	
1039	ranch	
1040	edible	

TEST

* 유의어와 반의어에 '0'이 있는 문제는 해당 어휘가 없는 경우이니 그냥 패스하시면 됩니다. 글자수의 (p.)는 '숙어' 표시입니다.

번호	유의어	반의어	영어	글자수
1041	climb, rise, mount	descend, fall	A	6
1042	expand, inflate, swell	Shrink, contract, compress	D	7
1043	essential, crucial, important	nonessential, insignificant, trivial	V	5
1044	Retirement income, annuity, stipend.	Employment, work, labor.	P	7
1045	nurture, cultivate, promote, encourage	hinder, impede, obstruct, block	F	6
1046	handle, use, exercise	relinquish, surrender, abandon	W	5
1047	Retrieve, Bring, Get	Leave, Abandon, Depart	F	5
1048	24/7, continuously	intermittently, occasionally	A	14 (p.)
1049	begin to do, start to do, undertake	avoid doing, refrain from doing, eschew doing	C	8 (p.)
1050	chicken, timid person, scaredy-cat	hero, brave, courageous	C	6
1051	regret, remorse, atone	Rejoice, celebrate, be content	R	6
1052	systematic, organized, orderly	Haphazard, disorganized, chaotic	M	10
1053	energetic, lively, vigorous	Static, motionless, unchanging	D	7
1054	make an impression on, influence, affect	Erase, remove, obliterate	L	12 (p.)
1055	Suspend, Cease, Pause	Continue, Persist, Uninterrupted	I	8
1056	compliment, praise, sweet-talk	insult, criticize	F	7
1057	contemplate, reflect, ponder	agitate, disturb	M	8
1058	similarly, likewise, in a similar manner	differently, dissimilarly, disparately	I	12 (p.)
1059	conversely, however	on the same side, likewise	O	13 (p.)
1060	Incline, slope, gradient, ascent.	Decline, Downturn	R	4

TEST

글자수의 (p.)는 '숙어' 표시입니다.

번호	영영	영어	글자수
1061	Attract or entice someone to do something, typically something unwise or wrong.	T	5
1062	Military weapons and equipment used for defense or warfare.	A	8
1063	To puncture or pierce.	P	5
1064	An instance of buying or selling.	T	11
1065	The background or setting behind something.	B	8
1066	Release or allow to leave.	L	6 (p.)
1067	during childhood or at a young age	A	12 (p.)
1068	incapable of producing offspring, crops, or results; unproductive and desolate	B	6
1069	continue or proceed with	C	7 (p.)
1070	Relating to the basic or fundamental principles or elements of a subject or field.	E	10
1071	endure or accept something, even if unpleasant	T	8
1072	A situation in which something dangerous or unpleasant was narrowly avoided.	C	9 (p.)
1073	to live in or occupy a place.	I	7
1074	To shock or greatly surprise; to fill with amazement.	A	7
1075	Doubtful, uncertain, or suspicious.	D	7
1076	not constrained or restricted by something	F	8 (p.)
1077	Not following a regular or predictable pattern; irregular.	E	7
1078	To entice or persuade someone into engaging in sexual activity or some other desired behavior.	S	6
1079	an amount or number of	A	11 (p.)
1080	Strong, healthy, and vigorous.	R	6

Day 19

TEST

번호	영어	한글
1081	in the coming year	
1082	compel	
1083	utter	
1084	commitment to N	
1085	recognize	
1086	contingent	
1087	crack	
1088	doctrine	
1089	restrict	
1090	aesthetic	
1091	derive	
1092	admit	
1093	be terrified of	
1094	acclimate	
1095	assert	
1096	coherent	
1097	crucial	
1098	combustion	
1099	submerge	
1100	perverse	

TEST

* 유의어와 반의어에 '0'이 있는 문제는 해당 어휘가 없는 경우이니 그냥 패스하시면 됩니다. 글자수의 (p.)는 '숙어' 표시입니다.

번호	유의어	반의어	영어	글자수
1101	Cut in line, skip ahead, bypass others in a line	Wait one's turn, stand in line, queue up	J	12 (p.)
1102	luxurious, lavish, opulent	basic, standard, ordinary	D	6
1103	donation, offering, gift	Withdrawal, subtraction, deduction	C	12
1104	struggle with, find it hard to, have trouble with	excel in, succeed in, thrive in	H	20 (p.)
1105	Math, calculation, figures, mathematics	Algebra, geometry, advanced math	A	10
1106	being considered, on the table	disregarded, ignored	U	18 (p.)
1107	be connected to, be affixed to	detach from, separate from	B	12 (p.)
1108	Unambiguous, clear, unequivocal	Ambiguous, vague, unclear	U	8
1109	innate, intrinsic, natural	acquired, learned	I	8
1110	have the ability to, be able to	be incapable of, unable to	B	11 (p.)
1111	uncertain, unresolved, pending	certain, definite, resolved	I	8 (p.)
1112	Abate, lessen, decrease, dwindle, taper off	Intensify, escalate, increase, worsen, amplify	S	7
1113	Postpone, delay, put off.	Expedite, advance, hasten.	D	5
1114	unemotional, detached, objective	Personal, individual, subjective	I	10
1115	contingent on, subject to	regardless of, irrespective of	D	11 (p.)
1116	stick, cling, attach	detach, disconnect	A	6
1117	Revengeful, vindictive, spiteful.	Forgiving, merciful, compassionate.	V	8
1118	deal with, handle, manage	succumb to, be overwhelmed by, be defeated by	C	8 (p.)
1119	gather, collect, convene	Disassemble, take apart, break down	A	8
1120	produce, generate, supply	resist, withhold, keep	Y	5

TEST

글자수의 (p.)는 '숙어' 표시입니다.

번호	영영	영어	글자수
1121	A large gathering or crowd.	C	9
1122	To eat something hungrily and quickly.	D	6
1123	A large quantity or plentiful supply of something.	A	8
1124	To beg or plead.	I	7
1125	To contribute to a particular result.	C	7
1126	ask for or obtain (something) without paying for it	M	5
1127	To distort or corrupt; also, a deviant person.	P	7
1128	Feeling a sense of urgency and despair, often due to extreme circumstances.	D	9
1129	to fall suddenly or clumsily; to roll or toss about.	T	6
1130	be afraid or scared of	B	14 (p.)
1131	To treat someone or something with cruelty or violence.	A	5
1132	To prevent something from happening.	A	5
1133	to put out or quench, especially a fire or flame.	E	10
1134	to completely destroy or eliminate something, especially pests or threats.	E	11
1135	an official order or decision issued by an authority	D	6
1136	a deceptive or misleading movement	F	5
1137	A short-lived and popular trend or fashion that quickly gains and loses popularity.	F	3
1138	to be careful	T	14 (p.)
1139	express strong disapproval or objection	P	7
1140	Having harmful intent.	M	10

Day 20

TEST

번호	영어	한글
1141	devote	
1142	unheard-of	
1143	pasture	
1144	deplore	
1145	at variance with	
1146	affiliate	
1147	innate	
1148	blast	
1149	violence	
1150	perspective	
1151	aspirator	
1152	acrophobia	
1153	append	
1154	smother	
1155	harass	
1156	clamorous	
1157	too much for	
1158	in the absence of	
1159	enlightenment	
1160	bury	

TEST

* 유의어와 반의어에 '0'이 있는 문제는 해당 어휘가 없는 경우이니 그냥 패스하시면 됩니다. 글자수의 (p.)는 '숙어' 표시입니다.

번호	유의어	반의어	영어	글자수
1161	own, have, hold	lack, be without	P	7
1162	compute, estimate, figure	guess, estimate, conjecture	C	9
1163	Wooing, dating, romance	Rejection, avoidance, indifference	C	9
1164	pelage, hair, coat	Skin, hide, pelage	F	3
1165	Consult, discuss	Ignore, disregard	C	6
1166	representative, envoy, proxy	Retain, keep, hold onto	D	8
1167	Follow, result, occur	Precede, antecede	E	5
1168	clan, ethnic group, community	Individual, person, single person	T	5
1169	Genocide, mass destruction, annihilation	Salvation, preservation, rescue	H	9
1170	assign, delegate, hand over	withhold, retain, keep	E	7
1171	scent, fragrance, smell	fragrance, scent, aroma	O	4
1172	on television, on the air	off the air, not broadcasting	O	9 (p.)
1173	Tool, implement, instrument	Raw material, resource, compone	U	7
1174	officer, policeman, lawman	criminal, lawbreaker	C	9
1175	songlike, poetic, melodious	instrumental, non-lyrical, wordless	L	5
1176	Paid by Someone, Funded by Another	At One's Own Expense, Self-financed	A	14 (p.)
1177	Hesitate, Waver, Stumble	Proceed, Advance, Persevere	F	6
1178	choice, option, substitute	Standard, common, regular	A	11
1179	genuine, real, legitimate	fake, counterfeit, fraudulent	A	9
1180	shortfall, shortage, deficiency	Surplus, excess, surplus	D	7

TEST

글자수의 (p.)는 '숙어' 표시입니다.

번호	영영	영어	글자수
1181	Empty or having a space inside.	H	6
1182	from a quick or superficial examination	A	13 (p.)
1183	conducive to or promoting good health and well-being.	W	9
1184	Strange, odd, or unconventional; also used as a derogatory term for LGBTQ+ individuals (use with caution).	Q	5
1185	A widespread occurrence of a disease or condition in a specific population or area.	E	8
1186	Implied or understood without being directly expressed.	I	8
1187	A child whose parents are dead.	O	6
1188	expecting a child; carrying a developing fetus.	P	8
1189	To assume control or responsibility.	T	8 (p.)
1190	most of the time or frequently	M	16 (p.)
1191	Move in a slow, heavy, awkward way.	L	6
1192	A branch of mathematics that deals with rates of change and accumulation, often used in calculus equations.	C	8
1193	Occurring naturally or without prior planning; impulsive.	S	11
1194	A person or creature much smaller than the average size.	D	5
1195	A body of voters in a specified area who elect a representative to a legislative body.	C	12
1196	A shape produced by a curve that bends around and crosses itself.	L	4
1197	the quality of being difficult to understand or catch	E	11
1198	To comply with established rules, standards, or norms; to act in accordance with expectations.	C	7
1199	The grammatical form indicating more than one item, person, or thing.	P	6
1200	To consign or dismiss to an inferior rank or position.	R	8

Day 21

TEST

번호	영어	한글
1201	varnish	
1202	stall	
1203	sewage	
1204	fertile	
1205	peculiar	
1206	frantic	
1207	at the outset	
1208	sleeve	
1209	avail oneself of	
1210	intimate	
1211	janitor	
1212	all the more	
1213	vanguard	
1214	extrinsic	
1215	pox	
1216	awkward	
1217	suffrage	
1218	exclaim	
1219	declaim	
1220	erode	

TEST

* 유의어와 반의어에 '0'이 있는 문제는 해당 어휘가 없는 경우이니 그냥 패스하시면 됩니다. 글자수의 (p.)는 '숙어' 표시입니다.

번호	유의어	반의어	영어	글자수
1221	height, elevation, altitude above sea level	depth, profundity, shallowness	A	8
1222	detest, loathe, hate, abhor	love, adore, cherish	A	9
1223	be compelled to do, be forced to do, have to do	have a choice not to do, be voluntary to do	H	19 (p.)
1224	Multimodal, multimedia, sensory	Nonvisual, nonauditory	A	11
1225	honor, prestige, respectability	disgrace, shame, dishonor	D	7
1226	harmonious, agreeable, compatible	Vowel, non-consonant, non-vocalic	C	9
1227	surpass, outdo, excel	lose, trail, fall behind	T	5
1228	universal, all-encompassing, comprehensive	Non-Catholic, non-denominational, non-religious	C	8
1229	candid, open, honest	dishonest, deceptive, insincere	F	5
1230	pull, drag, transport	push, leave, abandon	H	4
1231	District, locality, community, township.	Metropolis, city, urban area.	P	6
1232	calmness, tranquility, poise	agitation, anxiety, restlessness	C	9
1233	Brink, edge, threshold.	Center, middle, core.	V	5
1234	crash, impact, accident, collision, smash	avoidance, evasion, elusion, sidestepping, circumvention	C	9
1235	attribute, assign, credit	dissociate, separate	A	7
1236	fit, match, befit	mismatch, clash	S	4
1237	refrain, withhold, avoid	indulge, partake, engage	A	7
1238	Magnificent, grand, glorious, impressive.	Mediocre, ordinary, plain, unremarkable.	S	8
1239	empty, empty out, deplete	Fill, clog, block	D	5
1240	celebrate, be happy, delight	mourn, grieve, lament	R	7

TEST

글자수의 (p.)는 '숙어' 표시입니다.

번호	영영	영어	글자수
1241	grasp or seize firmly	C	11 (p.)
1242	Something that cannot be touched or physically perceived; often refers to abstract concepts.	I	10
1243	to formally introduce someone into a position or organization	I	6
1244	Lacking the ability to read or write; having limited or no literacy skills.	I	10
1245	a long, slender stick, typically made of wood, used as a support for walking or as a weapon	C	4
1246	To succeed or thrive, often in terms of wealth, growth, or well-being.	P	7
1247	firm or unyielding in one's beliefs or principles	S	9
1248	The flower or flowers of a plant, especially those of fruit trees.	B	7
1249	Cause (something unpleasant or painful) to be suffered by someone or something.	I	7
1250	A torn or tattered piece of cloth or fabric.	R	3
1251	to examine or scrutinize something closely.	I	7
1252	responsible for something wrong	A	7 (p.)
1253	The study of the Earth's atmosphere and weather.	M	11
1254	To publicly support or recommend a particular cause, policy, or action.	A	8
1255	beneficial or advantageous to someone	I	15 (p.)
1256	The act of sweating; moisture excreted through the sweat glands of the skin.	P	12
1257	Strong, robust, or physically sturdy.	S	5
1258	to set aside or commit something for a specific purpose or use; to devote time, effort, or resources to a cause or task	D	8
1259	Characterized by friendliness and goodwill.	A	8
1260	To prove something false.	C	7

Day 22

TEST

번호	영어	한글
1261	dismal	
1262	impeccable	
1263	unanimous	
1264	haze	
1265	at one's wit's end	
1266	answer for	
1267	puddle	
1268	slumber	
1269	linear	
1270	discriminate	
1271	fascinate	
1272	infer	
1273	strike a deal	
1274	displease	
1275	communism	
1276	miss a beat	
1277	in a series	
1278	confucius	
1279	for a change	
1280	resemble	

TEST

* 유의어와 반의어에 '0'이 있는 문제는 해당 어휘가 없는 경우이니 그냥 패스하시면 됩니다. 글자수의 (p.)는 '숙어' 표시입니다.

번호	유의어	반의어	영어	글자수
1281	clear, apparent, evident	hidden, concealed	O	7
1282	exceed, outperform, outdo	Lag behind, fall short, underperform	S	7
1283	emerge, occur, develop	subside, abate	A	5
1284	partnership, coalition, union	Enmity, rivalry, opposition	A	8
1285	immobile, fixed, motionless	moving, mobile	S	10
1286	fixate, preoccupy, haunt	detach, disconnect	O	6
1287	Pious, religious, faithful	Irreligious, atheistic, secular	D	6
1288	total, entire, comprehensive	net, partial, individual	G	5
1289	Violate, disobey, transgress, break, defy	Abide by, comply with, respect, obey, conform	C	10
1290	stop doing, discontinue, halt	continue to do, persist in doing, keep doing	C	9 (p.)
1291	achieve dual purposes, fulfill two objectives, meet two goals	Serve one purpose, be unidirectional	S	12 (p.)
1292	woodworker, joiner, craftsman	Non-carpenter, non-builder, non-artisan	C	9
1293	downgrade, reduce, lower	promote, advance, elevate	D	6
1294	a lot of, plenty of, a large amount of	a little of, a small amount of, a fraction of	A	12 (p.)
1295	spore, seed, dust	clean, purify, sterilize	P	6
1296	Nimble, quick, flexible	Clumsy, slow, rigid	A	5
1297	succeed, achieve, accomplish	fail, flop, fall short	C	7 (p.)
1298	finally, to sum up, in summary	in the introduction, in the beginning, initially	I	12 (p.)
1299	Based on, because of, due to.	Without cause, unjustly, unfairly.	O	14 (p.)
1300	blend into, combine into	separate from, disconnect from	M	9 (p.)

TEST

글자수의 (p.)는 '숙어' 표시입니다.

번호	영영	영어	글자수
1301	The possibility or capacity for future development or success; latent ability.	P	9
1302	seem to do	A	10 (p.)
1303	to cause someone to suffer or experience pain or distress	A	7
1304	other than doing something	E	10 (p.)
1305	Relating to conditions affecting public health, especially as a result of cleanliness and hygiene.	S	8
1306	To depict or represent someone or something in a particular way, often through art, words, or actions.	P	7
1307	Accept a difficult situation.	C	15 (p.)
1308	To be in a situation of urgency or shortage.	B	12 (p.)
1309	An official authorization, often in the form of a legal document, permitting a specific action or procedure.	W	7
1310	A distinct part or section of something that is separate or distinct from the whole.	S	7
1311	shared or experienced by two or more parties	M	6
1312	A disadvantage or negative aspect of a situation or decision.	D	8
1313	The maximum amount that something can hold or contain.	C	8
1314	An area or region, often with specific boundaries or characteristics.	D	8
1315	less than optimal; not as effective or efficient as possible	S	10
1316	Unclear, vague, or hidden from view.	O	7
1317	name or designate in honor of	C	9 (p.)
1318	apologize or justify one's actions	E	16 (p.)
1319	clean or clear an area by removing dirt or debris	D	5
1320	Financially prosperous or comfortable.	W	7 (p.)

Day 23

TEST

번호	영어	한글
1321	attempt	
1322	wreckage	
1323	at a discount	
1324	in awe of	
1325	detach	
1326	barometer	
1327	dipole	
1328	void	
1329	in a bid to do	
1330	omit	
1331	optical	
1332	nominate	
1333	coverage	
1334	wane	
1335	relish	
1336	intersperse	
1337	rebel	
1338	substitute A with B	
1339	statement	
1340	at length	

TEST

* 유의어와 반의어에 '0'이 있는 문제는 해당 어휘가 없는 경우이니 그냥 패스하시면 됩니다. 글자수의 (p.)는 '숙어' 표시입니다.

번호	유의어	반의어	영어	글자수
1341	Angry, upset	Calm, composed	H	17 (p.)
1342	strange, bizarre, peculiar	familiar, ordinary	O	10
1343	pragmatism, practicality, consequentialism	idealism, impracticality, non-utilitarianism	U	14
1344	reddish, rosy	pale, wan	R	5
1345	make up for lost time, get up to date on	fall behind on, lag behind in	C	9 (p.)
1346	sometimes, occasionally, from time to time	consistently, constantly, continually	A	7 (p.)
1347	candid, frank, forthright	reserved, quiet, reticent	O	9
1348	unavoidable, certain, inescapable	Avoidable, preventable, escapable	I	10
1349	renounce, reject, abandon, give up	assert, claim, own, acknowledge	D	8
1350	accumulative, collective, accrued	Isolated, separate, individual	C	10
1351	Grain, cereal	Dairy, meat	O	3
1352	blend in with, conform to, harmonize with	clash with, oppose, contradict	F	9 (p.)
1353	Cutting-edge, advanced, modern.	Outdated, obsolete, old-fashioned.	S	13 (p.)
1354	Emphasize, assert, argue	Minimize, downplay, ignore	M	16 (p.)
1355	pretend, imagine, simulate	reality, actuality, truth	M	11 (p.)
1356	real estate, property, land	illusion, fantasy	R	6
1357	Aeronautics, flight	Ground, land	A	8
1358	distance, range, extent from center	Diameter, width, breadth	R	6
1359	Residue, Remainder, Leftover	Whole, Entirety, Totality	R	7
1360	afraid of, frightened of, fearful of	unafraid of, fearless of, courageous in the face of	B	10 (p.)

TEST

글자수의 (p.)는 '숙어' 표시입니다.

번호	영영	영어	글자수
1361	give out or distribute something.	D	8
1362	The moral principles or values that guide behavior and decision-making.	E	6
1363	To move one's hand or a surface back and forth against something with pressure.	R	3
1364	To remain silent or refrain from speaking.	H	15 (p.)
1365	the act of flowing or coming in, especially of a liquid or substance, into a place or container	I	6
1366	Unusual, foreign, or strikingly different from what is familiar.	E	6
1367	a large and lavish meal or feast.	B	7
1368	Respectable, morally upright, or satisfactory.	D	6
1369	Offspring or descendants, collectively referring to one's children.	P	7
1370	To treat with contempt; despise.	C	7
1371	Dark or dim; having a dismal or depressing atmosphere.	G	6
1372	Important, noteworthy, or having a meaningful impact.	S	11
1373	having a mutual relationship or connection with something else	C	14 (p.)
1374	Completely vertical or steep, often used to describe cliffs or drops.	S	5
1375	Intense sadness or sorrow, especially due to a loss or tragedy.	G	5
1376	to confess or acknowledge that one is N	A	8 (p.)
1377	in advance of or before	A	7 (p.)
1378	A question or inquiry seeking information or clarification.	Q	5
1379	difficult to notice or understand	S	6
1380	To become smaller in size or quantity.	S	6

Day 24

TEST

번호	영어	한글
1381	plum	
1382	perplex	
1383	beguile	
1384	dissect	
1385	be prone to do	
1386	notate	
1387	overwhelm	
1388	relinquish	
1389	arrogant	
1390	flavor	
1391	prolong	
1392	persevere	
1393	ample	
1394	emit	
1395	draw A out	
1396	applaud	
1397	acknowledge	
1398	wither	
1399	fit A like a glove	
1400	provision	

TEST

* 유의어와 반의어에 '0'이 있는 문제는 해당 어휘가 없는 경우이니 그냥 패스하시면 됩니다. 글자수의 (p.)는 '숙어' 표시입니다.

번호	유의어	반의어	영어	글자수
1401	crawl, slither, sneak	Leap, jump, bound	C	5
1402	Duty, tax, customs	Exemption, rebate, discount	T	6
1403	strike, knock, hit	caress, stroke, pat	R	3
1404	equipment, machinery, device, instrument, tool	disorganization, chaos, disorder, confusion, disarray	A	9
1405	Memory loss, forgetfulness, blackout.	Memory retention, recollection.	A	7
1406	infuriate, enrage, anger	please, satisfy, appease	I	7
1407	Demonstrate, confirm, substantiate	Disprove, refute, invalidate	P	11 (p.)
1408	severe, rigorous, stern	gentle, mild, soft	H	5
1409	mourn, grieve, bemoan	celebrate, rejoice, applaud	L	6
1410	contaminated, tainted, impurities	Pure, uncontaminated, untainted	I	6
1411	regardless, regardless of, without regard to	considerate, mindful, concerned	I	12
1412	Complement, match	Clash, mismatch	G	10 (p.)
1413	withdraw, take back, revoke	Extend, prolong, maintain	R	7
1414	Be critical of, disapprove of, have a negative opinion of.	Be fond of, Approve	B	8 (p.)
1415	swear, imprecate, maledict	blessing, boon	C	5
1416	block, hinder, impede	facilitate, assist, aid	O	8
1417	native, indigenous person, original inhabitant	settler, immigrant	A	9
1418	initially, originally	eventually, finally	T	11 (p.)
1419	respiratory organ (in fish)	0	G	4
1420	mental health, psychological, psychotherapeutic, psychogenic	psychological, emotional, mental health, non-psychiatric	P	11

TEST

글자수의 (p.)는 '숙어' 표시입니다.

번호	영영	영어	글자수
1421	have the financial means to do	C	13 (p.)
1422	a place where deceased people are buried; a graveyard.	C	8
1423	to express sorrow or grief over a loss.	M	5
1424	to arrange in a straight line or correct relative positions; to bring into cooperation or agreement	A	5
1425	Titled or bearing a specific name.	O	6 (p.)
1426	An imaginary line that divides the Earth into northern and southern hemispheres, situated equidistant from the North and South Poles.	E	7
1427	A respiratory condition characterized by inflammation of the lungs.	P	9
1428	The speed of an object in a specific direction.	V	8
1429	specifically for or to someone	T	9 (p.)
1430	To redirect or change the course of something, often to a different destination or purpose.	D	6
1431	A state of balance, stability, or composure, both physically and mentally.	P	5
1432	Not honorable or noble in character; lacking moral or ethical principles.	I	7
1433	like or desire A more than B	P	10 (p.)
1434	infringe or go beyond the bounds of (a moral principle or other established standard of behavior)	T	10
1435	Rough or harsh in manner or texture.	A	8
1436	to save or keep something for future use	S	5
1437	Expressing that one action immediately follows another.	N	14 (p.)
1438	be greater in value or importance than something else	O	8
1439	Relating to an empire or an emperor; grand or majestic in scale.	I	8
1440	to go from one place to another.	M	10 (p.)

Day 25

TEST

번호	영어	한글
1441	intent on	
1442	colony	
1443	dew	
1444	work out	
1445	irritate	
1446	reprimand	
1447	in the face of	
1448	take a supplement	
1449	reap	
1450	diabetes	
1451	corrode	
1452	undue	
1453	primitive	
1454	assassinate	
1455	embody	
1456	embrace	
1457	resonant	
1458	mindlessly	
1459	pendulum	
1460	orchestrate	

TEST

* 유의어와 반의어에 '0'이 있는 문제는 해당 어휘가 없는 경우이니 그냥 패스하시면 됩니다. 글자수의 (p.)는 '숙어' 표시입니다.

번호	유의어	반의어	영어	글자수
1461	estrangement, isolation, detachment	Inclusion, integration, acceptance	A	10
1462	pole, spar, sail support	Bow, front, prow	M	4
1463	stare, look	glance, look away	G	4
1464	chaos, confusion, disorder, upheaval	calm, order, tranquility	T	7
1465	hide, cover, keep secret	reveal, uncover, expose	C	7
1466	merchandise, goods, products	Empty, vacant, bare	W	4
1467	Jungle fever, mosquito-borne illness.	Health, wellness, vitality.	M	7
1468	accommodate, house	evict, expel	L	5
1469	Earnings, income, revenue, profits.	Expenses, Losses	P	8
1470	ascend, rise, climb	descend, go down, lower	G	4 (p.)
1471	for this occasion, just this once	regularly, consistently, always	F	11 (p.)
1472	water, hydrate, moisten	Dehydrate, dry, drain	I	8
1473	tighten, squeeze, compress	expand, dilate, widen	C	9
1474	independently, by oneself, solo	with others, together, collectively	O	10 (p.)
1475	Ally, partner, accomplice.	Opponent, rival, enemy.	C	11
1476	copy, replicate, reproduce	Original, prototype, one-of-a-kind	D	9
1477	row, oar, boat	Stillness, immobility, inaction	P	6
1478	cunning, trickery, deceit	honesty, sincerity, truthfulness	A	8
1479	cruel, brutal, malicious	gentle, kind, benevolent	V	7
1480	Connection, link, relationship	Disconnection, separation, detachment	N	5

TEST

글자수의 (p.)는 '숙어' 표시입니다.

번호	영영	영어	글자수
1481	soak (meat, fish, or other food) in a marinade	M	8
1482	Relating to the surrounding environment or atmosphere.	A	7
1483	to continue firmly or obstinately in an opinion or a course of action	P	9 (p.)
1484	to accompany or complement something	G	6 (p.)
1485	to react to a provocation	R	13 (p.)
1486	materials used in schools, such as books, pens, pencils, and notebooks	S	14 (p.)
1487	occur at the same time or correspond with	C	12 (p.)
1488	Praise or express approval for someone's actions or qualities.	C	7
1489	to make something smooth, shiny, or refined through a process of cleaning or improvement.	P	6
1490	to become aware of something that one was not initially conscious of	C	12 (p.)
1491	Absolutely not; under no circumstances.	I	7 (p.)
1492	an alcohol produced by the fermentation of sugars or starches	E	7
1493	An observable event or occurrence, often with scientific or cultural significance.	P	10
1494	Having no strong feelings or interest, showing apathy or neutrality.	I	11
1495	to be certain of something	M	18 (p.)
1496	To agree or consent to a demand, request, or treaty.	A	6
1497	To prove something to be false or incorrect.	R	6
1498	have a harmonious or friendly relationship with	G	12 (p.)
1499	Acting hastily or without careful consideration; a skin eruption.	R	4
1500	To integrate or absorb information, ideas, or cultures.	A	10

Day 26

TEST

번호	영어	한글
1501	contour	
1502	vertical	
1503	strife	
1504	do with	
1505	in an effort to do	
1506	on closer inspection	
1507	cacophony	
1508	merchant	
1509	render	
1510	be on the point of -ing	
1511	hypothesis	
1512	be detached from	
1513	latitude	
1514	expire	
1515	hand down	
1516	anomy	
1517	spatial	
1518	substitute	
1519	get into trouble	
1520	at a charge of	

TEST

* 유의어와 반의어에 '0'이 있는 문제는 해당 어휘가 없는 경우이니 그냥 패스하시면 됩니다. 글자수의 (p.)는 '숙어' 표시입니다.

번호	유의어	반의어	영어	글자수
1521	Criminal, thief	Law-abiding citizen	C	5
1522	banish, deport, expel	inclusion, acceptance	E	5
1523	declare, claim, assert	Deny, renounce, disclaim	P	7
1524	Pre-war, Before the war	Post-war, After the war	A	10
1525	demand, assert, affirm	acquiesce, yield, concede	I	6
1526	obsessive, addictive, uncontrollable	voluntary, optional	C	10
1527	observe, watch, witness	ignore, overlook, disregard	L	6 (p.)
1528	Eliminate, eradicate, annul	Establish, institute, retain	A	7
1529	naked, exposed, uncovered	clothed, covered, concealed	I	8 (p.)
1530	compliant, submissive, dutiful	Disobedient, rebellious, defiant	O	8
1531	fake, pretend, simulate	reveal, show, display	F	5
1532	worldly, sophisticated, cultured	provincial, narrow-minded, parochial	C	12
1533	stress, tension, pressure	ease, relax	S	6
1534	decode, interpret, translate	encode, encrypt, confuse	D	8
1535	disconnect, sever, detach	connect, link, join	C	6 (p.)
1536	persistent, long-term, constant	acute, sudden	C	7
1537	eliminate, remove, excise	add in, insert, include	C	6 (p.)
1538	mutual, shared, corresponding	one-sided, unilateral, non-reciprocal	R	10
1539	Assume, suppose, conjecture.	Doubt, question, dispute.	P	7
1540	shortage, lack, insufficiency	Abundance, plentifulness, profusion	S	8

TEST

글자수의 (p.)는 '숙어' 표시입니다.

번호	영영	영어	글자수
1541	To locate or find after searching or pursuing.	T	9 (p.)
1542	Bring or recall a feeling, memory, or image to the conscious mind.	E	5
1543	extract or remove A	G	7 (p.)
1544	to draw attention to something; to announce or mention publicly	A	6
1545	To take action to achieve something.	T	12 (p.)
1546	To indicate or symbolize a specific meaning or concept.	D	6
1547	A hidden or unexpected danger or difficulty.	P	7
1548	susceptible to harm or damage from N	V	13 (p.)
1549	To compensate for the faults or bad aspects of something.	R	6
1550	To become overly focused or obsessed with a particular idea, object, or person.	F	6
1551	An animal or organism that hunts and preys on other organisms for food.	P	8
1552	Regardless; nevertheless.	I	10 (p.)
1553	Close by or readily available.	A	6 (p.)
1554	To force someone to leave or eject them from a place, organization, or group.	E	5
1555	To incite or inspire action or response; to cause something to happen quickly.	P	6
1556	Separated from or existing without a body.	D	11
1557	Almost or nearly.	A	6 (p.)
1558	Widespread recognition and reputation, often resulting from notable achievements.	F	4
1559	strongly encourage or persuade	U	4
1560	Dealing with things sensibly and realistically in a way that is based on practical rather than theoretical considerations.	P	9

Day 27

TEST

번호	영어	한글
1561	in the ratio of	
1562	complacent	
1563	lest	
1564	gravel	
1565	dehydrate	
1566	extricate	
1567	spouse	
1568	optimal	
1569	have a discussion with	
1570	take place	
1571	pious	
1572	proclaim	
1573	naturalize	
1574	invest A with B	
1575	dose	
1576	hold back	
1577	fatigue	
1578	digest	
1579	none the worse	
1580	augment	

TEST

* 유의어와 반의어에 '0'이 있는 문제는 해당 어휘가 없는 경우이니 그냥 패스하시면 됩니다. 글자수의 (p.)는 '숙어' 표시입니다.

번호	유의어	반의어	영어	글자수
1581	at the start of, initially, in the early stages of	at the end of, in the middle of, midway through	A	16 (p.)
1582	waiting, pending, in abeyance, in suspense	active, ongoing, in progress, underway	O	6 (p.)
1583	remove A, clear A, eliminate A	bring A forward, facilitate A, encourage A	G	15 (p.)
1584	considering A and B, due to A and B	regardless of A and B, despite A and B	W	13 (p.)
1585	reduce, diminish, decrease	intensify, increase, amplify	L	6
1586	regional language, vernacular, accent	standard language, common speech	D	7
1587	adjust to N, acclimate to N	resist N, oppose N	A	8 (p.)
1588	sluggish, inactive, still, motionless	active, dynamic, vigorous, brisk	S	8
1589	swiftness, speed	slowness, delay	C	8
1590	Facilitate, enable, assist, help, promote	Hinder, impede, obstruct, prevent, thwart	S	9 (p.)
1591	overstate, inflate, embellish	minimize, downplay	E	10
1592	destroy, ruin, devastate	Rebuild, restore, reconstruct	D	9
1593	compulsory, required, obligatory	Optional, voluntary, discretionary	M	9
1594	reason, cause, purpose	Detriment, harm, disadvantage	S	4
1595	smudge, daub, spread	clean, wipe	S	5
1596	Pass, spend, occupy (time)	Be productive, make the most of, utilize (time)	W	9 (p.)
1597	ridiculous, nonsensical	logical, sensible	A	6
1598	Address, tackle, deal with, confront.	Ignore, avoid, neglect.	T	14 (p.)
1599	influence, impact, sway	effect, influence, impact	A	6
1600	Transmission, conveyance, passage, transfer.	Absorption, obstruction, blocking.	T	13

TEST

글자수의 (p.)는 '숙어' 표시입니다.

번호	영영	영어	글자수
1601	not in accordance with established rules or regulations	A	14 (p.)
1602	Prejudice, discrimination, or antagonism directed against someone of a different race based on the belief in the inherent superiority of one's own race.	R	6
1603	free of charge or without payment	A	8 (p.)
1604	A straight line joining two opposite corners of a square, rectangle, or other straight-sided shape.	D	8
1605	A discrete quantity of energy proportional to the frequency of the radiation it represents.	Q	7
1606	To remove or take back something; to retreat or remove oneself from a situation or place.	W	8
1607	to commit to or start a task or project.	U	9
1608	bring to an end or conclude	T	9
1609	adapt or modify oneself to fit N	A	9 (p.)
1610	essential or necessary	I	10
1611	The soft substance consisting of muscle and fat that is found between the skin and bones.	F	5
1612	a new word or phrase, especially one that has been created recently	N	9
1613	Showing fear or lack of confidence; timid.	T	8
1614	Serious, formal, and dignified in manner or tone; often associated with a significant event or ceremony.	S	6
1615	intense, violent anger or rage	F	4
1616	to delight or captivate someone with charm, beauty, or magic; to cast a spell on	E	7
1617	A sudden, sharp increase in something.	S	5
1618	Solely, exclusively; indicating there is nothing else except the specified thing.	N	10 (p.)
1619	to be next to or connected to something	A	6
1620	To consider or include A in the decision or analysis.	T	16 (p.)

Day 28

TEST

번호	영어	한글
1621	initiate	
1622	flush	
1623	have only to do	
1624	in good faith	
1625	bear with	
1626	abridge	
1627	competent	
1628	causal	
1629	to the core	
1630	recur	
1631	take up	
1632	speak of the devil	
1633	gasp	
1634	shorthand	
1635	in a daze	
1636	hospitality	
1637	impede	
1638	precedent	
1639	archaeology	
1640	equipped with	

TEST

* 유의어와 반의어에 '0'이 있는 문제는 해당 어휘가 없는 경우이니 그냥 패스하시면 됩니다. 글자수의 (p.)는 '숙어' 표시입니다.

번호	유의어	반의어	영어	글자수
1641	Reduce, decrease, lessen	Increase, grow, expand	D	8
1642	respond, return, counter, exchange, mutual	ignore, reject, disregard, spurn, avoid	R	11
1643	involve, necessitate, require	exclude, omit, disregard	E	6
1644	Deplete, drain, exhaust	Enrich, prosper, wealthify	I	10
1645	Flock, group, crowd, swarm, pack, shoal, pride	Individual, lone, solitary, isolated, detached	H	4
1646	resolve, clarify, organize	confuse, complicate, muddle	S	7 (p.)
1647	board, panel, council	Individual, separate, non-committee	C	9
1648	prohibition, restriction, ban	Acceptable, permissible, allowed	T	5
1649	wager, bet, investment	forfeit, surrender, lose	S	5
1650	Dispute, disagreement, contention	Agreement, consensus, harmony	C	11
1651	looking for, seeking, searching for	Found, discovered, located	I	10 (p.)
1652	moon-related, moonlit, moonlike	Solar, earthly, terrestrial	L	5
1653	legislature, congress, governing body	Non-parliament, non-legislative body, non-congress	P	10
1654	Halt, interrupt, cease	Continue, resume, proceed	S	7
1655	Evangelist, Preacher, Proselytizer	Non-believer, Heathen, Unconverted	M	10
1656	slander, defame, vilify, criticize	praise, compliment, endorse, support	M	6
1657	Deceive, disloyal, backstab	Loyalty, faithfulness, honesty	B	6
1658	Destitution, indigence, penury	Wealth, affluence, prosperity	P	7
1659	bite, prick, puncture	soothe, relieve, calm	S	5
1660	inform, tell	keep the news from, conceal the news from	B	14 (p.)

TEST

글자수의 (p.)는 '숙어' 표시입니다.

번호	영영	영어	글자수
1661	Lacking in sensitivity or good taste.	I	10
1662	A sudden and temporary interruption in the supply of a service or utility.	O	6
1663	prevent or restrain someone from doing something	I	7
1664	to be good at something	B	11 (p.)
1665	to care for and encourage the growth and development of someone or something; to foster or support	N	7
1666	To start or begin doing something seriously or with determination.	G	9 (p.)
1667	become involved in or start participating in	E	9 (p.)
1668	A thick, dark oil obtained from under the ground, from which various substances (e.g., gasoline) are produced.	P	9
1669	Income generated by a business, organization, or government through its operations.	R	7
1670	Being on time or arriving at the scheduled time.	P	8
1671	an animal that feeds on dead or waste organic matter.	S	9
1672	Moving or happening quickly; fast in action or speed.	S	5
1673	Used to express that B is more applicable or relevant than A.	N	13 (p.)
1674	To refrain or abstain.	F	7
1675	To overcome or defeat.	G	14 (p.)
1676	A feeling of discomfort, anxiety, or tension; a sense of being unsettled or uneasy.	U	6
1677	to expel air suddenly and involuntarily from the nose and mouth, often in response to irritation or illness	S	6
1678	On fire; burning brightly.	A	6
1679	Involved with others in an illegal activity or wrongdoing.	C	9
1680	Being the most common or influential in a particular situation.	P	11

Day 29

TEST

번호	영어	한글
1681	so long as	
1682	execute	
1683	revoke	
1684	jest	
1685	confess	
1686	obtain	
1687	round the clock	
1688	populist	
1689	indigenous	
1690	nourish	
1691	sage	
1692	magnificent	
1693	avocation	
1694	impair	
1695	behalf	
1696	condense	
1697	cast A aside	
1698	write a good hand	
1699	meadow	
1700	come across	

TEST

* 유의어와 반의어에 '0'이 있는 문제는 해당 어휘가 없는 경우이니 그냥 패스하시면 됩니다. 글자수의 (p.)는 '숙어' 표시입니다.

번호	유의어	반의어	영어	글자수
1701	admiration, reverence, wonder	indifference, apathy, disregard	A	3
1702	barren, bleak, deserted	Inhabited, populated, thriving	D	8
1703	remorseful, contrite, regretful	unrepentant, impenitent, defiant	P	8
1704	ratio, percentage, fraction	Disproportion, imbalance, inequality	P	10
1705	thief, intruder, robber	homeowner, resident	B	7
1706	At its peak, at its maximum, at its zenith	At its lowest, at its minimum, at its nadir	A	12 (p.)
1707	spot, discern	overlook, ignore	D	6
1708	imperil, jeopardize, threaten	protect, safeguard	E	8
1709	exclude, leave out	include, incorporate	I	10 (p.)
1710	frosting, glaze, icing sugar	Dry, unfrosted, unglazed	I	5
1711	inherent, innate, essential	extrinsic, external, acquired	I	9
1712	restrict, limit, enclose	release, free	C	7
1713	deduct, take away, minus	Add, increase, augment	S	8
1714	spontaneous, extemporaneous, unrehearsed	planned, rehearsed, prepared	I	9
1715	offspring, descendants, heirs	ancestors, forebears, predecessors	P	8
1716	in touch with, connected with, communicating with	isolated from, separate from, disconnected from	I	13 (p.)
1717	gulp, ingest, consume	spit out, expel	S	7
1718	refer, hint, suggest, imply	specify, state, mention, point out	A	6
1719	surrender, yield, give in, collapse	resist, withstand, endure, survive	S	7
1720	committee, assembly, board	individual, person	C	7

TEST

글자수의 (p.)는 '숙어' 표시입니다.

번호	영영	영어	글자수
1721	attract interest or support	A	9 (p.)
1722	A collection of historical documents or records.	A	7
1723	to give (control, responsibility, authority, etc.) to someone	D	12 (p.)
1724	Natural ability or talent for a particular activity, skill, or field.	A	8
1725	Inactive or characterized by prolonged sitting.	S	9
1726	someone who supports or defends a particular cause or idea.	P	9
1727	The consequences or results of a significant event.	A	9
1728	stretched or rigid	T	5
1729	sudden and unexpected; characterized by a sharp change.	A	6
1730	to reverse or cancel the effects of something that has been done; to unfasten or untie	U	4
1731	To change or transform from one state, belief, or condition to another.	C	7
1732	capable of being transmitted from one person or thing to another	C	10
1733	To happen at the same time or to align in terms of events or positions.	C	8
1734	retreat or withdraw from a position or stance	B	8 (p.)
1735	not able to exist together	M	17 (p.)
1736	To get involved in a situation or activity where one is not wanted or needed.	I	9
1737	be experienced or encountered suddenly or unexpectedly	F	6 (p.)
1738	Tedious or unpleasant work.	D	8
1739	To allow oneself to enjoy or partake in something pleasurable, often in excess.	I	7
1740	A person who is lower in rank or position within an organization or hierarchy.	S	11

Day 30

TEST

번호	영어	한글
1741	memorabilia	
1742	rejuvenate	
1743	bruise	
1744	census	
1745	banish	
1746	deduction	
1747	stride	
1748	attire	
1749	worship	
1750	retail	
1751	empathic	
1752	cognitive	
1753	put A to death	
1754	what is more	
1755	vanish	
1756	status quo	
1757	get past	
1758	hop	
1759	sequel	
1760	condone	

TEST

* 유의어와 반의어에 '0'이 있는 문제는 해당 어휘가 없는 경우이니 그냥 패스하시면 됩니다. 글자수의 (p.)는 '숙어' 표시입니다.

번호	유의어	반의어	영어	글자수
1761	metabolic, bodily, physiological	Nonmetabolic, inactive, dormant	M	9
1762	outline, profile, contour	detail, elaboration, intricacy	S	10
1763	pitiful, miserable, wretched	impressive, admirable	P	8
1764	small, trivial, minor, insignificant	significant, important, substantial	P	5
1765	standing, upright, on foot	off one's feet, sitting, lying down	O	11 (p.)
1766	Bully, frighten, threaten, coerce.	Comfort, Reassure	I	10
1767	Pledge, Vow, Promise	Denial, Refusal, Renunciation	O	4
1768	Donate to, Give to, Provide for	Withhold from, Keep from, Deprive of	C	13 (p.)
1769	Authority over, command, mastery	Lack of control, powerlessness, submission	C	11 (p.)
1770	cynic, downbeat, defeatist	optimist, positive thinker	P	9
1771	divert, sidetrack, disrupt	Focus, concentrate, pay attention	D	8
1772	be cautious, be alert, take care	trust, believe, rely	B	6
1773	metallic element, metal, can	Valuable metal, precious metal, superior metal	T	3
1774	produce, make, fabricate	Unmake, disassemble, break down	M	11
1775	fearful, anxious, jittery	calm, composed, confident	T	6
1776	hallway, passage, aisle	open space, courtyard, field	C	8
1777	boy, youth, youngster	girl, lass	L	3
1778	cancel, invalidate	validate, approve	A	5
1779	expect, predict, foresee	overlook, disregard, ignore	A	10
1780	order, series, arrangement	Disarray, randomness, chaos	S	8

TEST

글자수의 (p.)는 '숙어' 표시입니다.

번호	영영	영어	글자수
1781	Considering or taking into account.	I	12 (p.)
1782	To give the impression of being a certain way.	C	12 (p.)
1783	To establish a practice or habit of doing something regularly.	M	15 (p.)
1784	Significantly or extensively.	I	9 (p.)
1785	To extinguish or put out, often referring to a candle or flame.	S	5
1786	To express disapproval or criticism; to scold or rebuke someone for their actions.	R	7
1787	to tremble or shake involuntarily due to fear, cold, or disgust.	S	6
1788	someone's preferred taste or interest	C	8 (p.)
1789	Self-restraint, especially in resisting impulses or desires.	C	10
1790	to declare someone not guilty of a crime	A	6
1791	to stay informed about the latest developments or information	K	12 (p.)
1792	To give someone incorrect or false information, leading them to believe something that is not true.	M	7
1793	Deceptive or dishonest behavior intended to gain an unfair or unlawful advantage, often involving deception for financial gain.	F	5
1794	not affected or influenced by N; resistant to N	I	9 (p.)
1795	To cause distress or suffering.	A	8
1796	The highest degree or most extreme point.	U	6
1797	To greatly surprise or amaze someone.	A	8
1798	To officially or formally remove someone from a position or role.	D	7
1799	Having more than one possible interpretation or meaning; unclear or vague.	A	9
1800	To plant seeds in the ground for the purpose of growing crops.	S	3

Day 31

TEST

번호	영어	한글
1801	summit	
1802	evade	
1803	parable	
1804	in decline	
1805	snore	
1806	by turns	
1807	in common with	
1808	mash	
1809	encounter	
1810	privilege	
1811	chubby	
1812	aspiration	
1813	deplete	
1814	heir	
1815	draw on	
1816	propel	
1817	longitude	
1818	vessel	
1819	at a 형 price	
1820	end up	

TEST

* 유의어와 반의어에 '0'이 있는 문제는 해당 어휘가 없는 경우이니 그냥 패스하시면 됩니다. 글자수의 (p.)는 '숙어' 표시입니다.

번호	유의어	반의어	영어	글자수
1821	calm, tranquil, serene	in turmoil, unsettled, disturbed	A	7 (p.)
1822	long life, duration, permanence	brevity, short life, transience	L	9
1823	Disturb, disrupt, disarrange.	Arrange, organize, order.	D	7
1824	retain, grasp, keep	release, let go, relinquish	H	8 (p.)
1825	story, tale, narrative	Fact, reality, truth	A	8
1826	attribute A to B, hold B responsible for A	absolve A from B, exonerate A for	B	9 (p.)
1827	set free, liberate, unleash	hold, retain	R	7
1828	ascribe, assign, credit	dissociate, disconnect	A	9
1829	motivate, encourage, influence	Discourage, demotivate, dishearten	I	7
1830	stitch, stitch up, mend	rip, tear	S	3
1831	Indifference, disinterest, apathetic.	Enthusiasm, interest, passion.	A	6
1832	unused, undeveloped, unexplored	Utilized, exploited, harnessed	U	8
1833	flaw, imperfection, fault	asset, advantage	D	6
1834	According to, based on, in proportion to	Irrespective of, regardless of, uniformly	A	11 (p.)
1835	Prohibit, Forbid, Ban	Allow, Permit, Authorize	I	9
1836	region, territory, area, domain, district	metropolis, urban area, city, megalopolis, cosmopolitan area	P	8
1837	standard, guideline, parameter	Irrelevant factor, non-factor, irrelevant aspect	C	9
1838	Modest, humble, unpretentious, low-key.	Pretentious, Arrogant	U	10
1839	student, learner, scholar	teacher, instructor, educator	P	5
1840	compete for, vie for, campaign for, seek reelection for	withdraw from, drop out, resign from	R	6 (p.)

TEST

글자수의 (p.)는 '숙어' 표시입니다.

번호	영영	영어	글자수
1841	Make a low, mournful sound expressing pain, discomfort, or unhappiness.	M	4
1842	To provide a firm foundation or support for something.	U	8
1843	to get rid of or deal with something	D	9 (p.)
1844	To successfully complete a task or achieve a goal.	A	10
1845	a dead body	C	6
1846	be responsible or accountable for	B	12 (p.)
1847	the backbone of an animal.	S	5
1848	to agree with or support something	A	9 (p.)
1849	At least and a minimum of.	N	10 (p.)
1850	return to a former or less developed state	R	7
1851	The fundamental physical and organizational structures and facilities needed for the operation of a society, such as roads, bridges, utilities, and communication systems.	I	14
1852	make provisions or considerations for	A	8 (p.)
1853	Excessive and insatiable desire for wealth, possessions, or power.	G	5
1854	The cultural, historical, or natural legacy passed down from one generation to the next.	H	8
1855	To make up for a loss or deficiency; to provide with something beneficial.	C	10
1856	To change the direction, order, or course of something to its opposite.	R	7
1857	To assist, support, or encourage someone in carrying out a wrongdoing.	A	4
1858	leave furtively or unnoticed	S	8 (p.)
1859	to deny or disagree with a statement or assertion.	C	10
1860	To deceive or trick someone, often for personal gain.	C	3

Day 32

TEST

번호	영어	한글
1861	correspond to N	
1862	enjoin	
1863	rhetorical	
1864	moral	
1865	prone	
1866	degenerate	
1867	consort	
1868	bewilder	
1869	gut	
1870	behold	
1871	insure	
1872	potable	
1873	peer	
1874	compound	
1875	carbon footprint	
1876	sophisticated	
1877	intrepid	
1878	valid	
1879	be divided into	
1880	impartial	

TEST

* 유의어와 반의어에 '0'이 있는 문제는 해당 어휘가 없는 경우이니 그냥 패스하시면 됩니다. 글자수의 (p.)는 '숙어' 표시입니다.

번호	유의어	반의어	영어	글자수
1881	interfere, meddle	mind one's own business, abstain	P	17 (p.)
1882	complexify, entangle, confuse	simplify, clarify	C	10
1883	Authority, control, power	Subjection, submission, obedience	J	12
1884	send, transmit, convey	receive, accept, take in	D	8
1885	act involuntarily, act reluctantly	act willingly, voluntarily	A	19 (p.)
1886	slide, coast, soar	stumble, trip	G	5
1887	have influence, hold sway, be significant, be important	lack influence, be inconsequential, be unimportant	C	11 (p.)
1888	Invasion, intrusion, attack	Retreat, withdrawal, departure	I	9
1889	Breathless, panting, winded	Breathable, at ease, relaxed	S	13 (p.)
1890	overweight, corpulence, heaviness	thinness, slenderness, leanness	O	7
1891	chest, bosom, bust	Back, rear	B	6
1892	fantastic, excellent, wonderful	awful, terrible	T	8
1893	strange, unusual, bizarre	normal, ordinary, conventional	W	5
1894	trapped in, ensnared in, entangled in	free from, liberated from, released from	C	8 (p.)
1895	mumble, whisper, mutter	shout, yell	M	6
1896	obstructing, blocking, hindering	out of the way, clear, unobstructed	I	8 (p.)
1897	Middle Ages, ancient, historical	Modern, contemporary, current	M	8
1898	weak, feeble, faint-hearted	strong, bold	F	5
1899	Intersection, connection, meeting point	Separation, disconnection, divergence	J	8
1900	assume A, presume A, expect A	appreciate A, value A, cherish A	T	15 (p.)

TEST

글자수의 (p.)는 '숙어' 표시입니다.

번호	영영	영어	글자수
1901	Cunning or deceitful behavior.	G	5
1902	To conclude or finish something.	B	10 (p.)
1903	Preventing success or development; harmful; unfavorable.	A	7
1904	an insult or disrespectful treatment	A	7
1905	Having its origins or foundation in something.	R	8 (p.)
1906	Following in uninterrupted order, one after another.	C	11
1907	Request assistance.	A	11 (p.)
1908	diminish or decline gradually	F	8 (p.)
1909	to divide into two equal parts; to cut in half.	H	5
1910	On display for public viewing.	O	9 (p.)
1911	familiar or knowledgeable about a particular subject	C	10
1912	currently or presently	A	11 (p.)
1913	A person who is authorized to perform religious duties and lead worship in a church or religious organization, or a government official responsible for a specific department or area.	M	8
1914	A branch of mathematics dealing with symbols and their operations.	A	7
1915	To make a low, continuous sound, often like a buzz.	H	3
1916	A place where monks or nuns live, work, and worship as part of a religious community.	M	9
1917	a sample or example of something	S	8
1918	To secretly plan together to commit an illegal or harmful act.	C	8
1919	to combine or associate A with B	C	12 (p.)
1920	to experience a sudden failure or collapse	H	14 (p.)

Day 33

TEST

번호	영어	한글
1921	favoritism	
1922	delinquent	
1923	senator	
1924	tactful	
1925	be familiar with	
1926	stun	
1927	averse	
1928	work on	
1929	tremendous	
1930	A rather than B	
1931	correspond	
1932	absorb	
1933	lay the foundation	
1934	apprehend	
1935	virgin	
1936	expedition	
1937	tragic	
1938	reindeer	
1939	humiliate	
1940	immerse	

TEST

* 유의어와 반의어에 '0'이 있는 문제는 해당 어휘가 없는 경우이니 그냥 패스하시면 됩니다. 글자수의 (p.)는 '숙어' 표시입니다.

번호	유의어	반의어	영어	글자수
1941	begin, start, initiate	conclude, finish	C	8
1942	interrupt, interject	break out, escape from	B	7 (p.)
1943	isolate, protect, shield	Conduct, transfer, transmit	I	8
1944	guide, direct, navigate	drift, meander	S	5
1945	crave, desire, long	despise, loathe, detest	Y	5
1946	contradiction, puzzle, enigma	Consistency, agreement, conformity	P	7
1947	pain, torment, suffering	comfort, ease, pleasure	A	5
1948	consider, meditate, reflect	neglect, disregard	C	11
1949	be likely to, have a good chance of, be poised to, be in a position to	avoid, evade, shun, escape, ignore	S	9 (p.)
1950	For the benefit of, for the sake of, in favor of.	Against the interests of, Detrimental to	I	16 (p.)
1951	tear, rip, slice	assemble, unite, join	S	5
1952	Journey, trip, expedition	Stay, remain, stagnation	V	6
1953	attribute A to B, credit B with A, ascribe A to B	be indebted to B, be obligated to B, be beholden to B	O	7 (p.)
1954	undergo N, experience N, endure N	be shielded from N, be protected from N, be defended from N	B	14 (p.)
1955	cut, clip, prune	expand, enlarge, lengthen	T	4
1956	financial, fiscal, economic	Non-monetary, non-financial, non-cash	M	8
1957	Far away, remotely, distantly, from a distance	Up close, nearby, closely	A	11 (p.)
1958	thoughtful, contemplative, reflective	carefree, unreflective, thoughtless	P	7
1959	boomerang, rebound, misfire	Succeed, go well, work out	B	8
1960	separation, division, isolation	integration, inclusion	S	11

TEST

글자수의 (p.)는 '숙어' 표시입니다.

번호	영영	영어	글자수
1961	consume as nourishment or sustenance	F	6 (p.)
1962	To obey or adhere to rules, instructions, or requests.	C	6
1963	go away or depart, especially permanently	T	9 (p.)
1964	engage in dishonest or immoral behavior; cause to become dishonest or impure	C	7
1965	an action or act; a legal document representing ownership.	D	4
1966	Comprehensive or all-inclusive.	O	7
1967	to produce offspring through reproduction; a specific type or category of something	B	5
1968	Owing money or being financially obligated to someone or an institution.	I	6
1969	Because of various factors or circumstances.	W	26 (p.)
1970	Almost or nearly, but not completely.	L	13 (p.)
1971	be intended or directed towards a particular goal or target	B	9 (p.)
1972	To make someone or something numb or insensitive.	B	6
1973	A disagreement or argument.	D	7
1974	Illegitimate or born out of wedlock; a derogatory term for an unpleasant person.	B	7
1975	The layer of gases surrounding a planet, including Earth, that is held in place by gravity.	A	10
1976	feel proud of or derive satisfaction from	T	11 (p.)
1977	Out of necessity; because it is necessary.	O	11 (p.)
1978	to fill something with something else	I	10
1979	lasting forever or for a very long time.	P	9
1980	To come together or meet at a common point.	C	8

Day 34

TEST

번호	영어	한글
1981	integrate A with B	
1982	declare	
1983	convict	
1984	definite	
1985	depict	
1986	altruism	
1987	exclusive	
1988	call off	
1989	amid	
1990	take with	
1991	triumph over	
1992	proficient	
1993	thrift	
1994	act upon	
1995	in a word	
1996	resist	
1997	invaluable	
1998	get into shape	
1999	gulf	
2000	arrogate	

Answers.

Day 1

page 4

번호	정답
1	a. 아직 해결되지 않은, 보류 중인
2	a. 거대한, 엄청난, 막대한
3	v. 초래하다; (손실을) 입다, (빚을) 지다
4	a. 무자비한, 냉정한
5	p. 많은
6	p. 자리를 잡다, 확립하다, 정착하다
7	n. 찡그림 v. 눈살을 찌푸리다
8	p. ~을 의식하다, ~을 알고 있다
9	p. 편을 들다
10	p. A와 안면은 있다
11	v. 울다, 슬퍼하다
12	p. 같은 부류인
13	v. 진행하다 n. 판매 또는 거래의 수익
14	n. 곡예사, (정치적 의견, 주의 등의) 변절자
15	n. 친척, 친족; 친족인
16	v. 단념하다, 그만두다
17	v. 핥다
18	v. 기념하다, 기념식을 거행하다
19	a. 적대적인, 공격적인
20	v. 보존하다, 보호하다

page 5

번호	정답
21	have a hand in
22	enclosure
23	cottage
24	solvent
25	recondition
26	consent
27	pervade
28	grasp
29	fallacy
30	cradle
31	sneak
32	allure
33	pity
34	picket
35	parachute
36	timber
37	shovel
38	recover from
39	reflect
40	at the age of

page 6

번호	정답
41	at the height of
42	cohere
43	exploit
44	magnetism
45	nod
46	embed
47	thorn
48	bring to the table
49	as ever
50	have something to do with
51	eccentric
52	pregnable
53	slay
54	satire
55	shed
56	drown
57	levy
58	sermon
59	sparse
60	omen

Day 2

page 8

번호	정답
61	v. 삼켜버리다
62	p. (책 등의) 목차
63	n. 악필
64	n. 연금술, 신비한 힘, 마력
65	v. 붙잡아두다
66	a. 비참한, 비열한
67	v. 원상태로 돌리다, 사회에 복귀시키다
68	v. 곰곰이 생각하다, 심사숙고하다
69	n. 얼간이, 멍청이, 바보
70	p. ~에 관심이 있다
71	p. 가슴에 뼈저리게 사무치다
72	v. 구성하다
73	p. ~을 구조하러 오다
74	a. 맞닿아 있는, 인접한; 연속된
75	p. A를 염두에 두고
76	n. 탄력성, 회복력
77	n. 보충, 보충물; 보어
78	a. 싫어하는, 꺼리는
79	v. (법률을) 제정하다, 규정하다
80	p. 가까이에

page 9

번호	정답
81	reimburse
82	ornament
83	rhinoceros
84	extort
85	orbit
86	in a crow line
87	at a low price
88	advent
89	in a degree
90	digress
91	exhaust
92	cannot too
93	hand in
94	conspicuous
95	grudge
96	stitch
97	shrug
98	sway
99	rustic
100	frugal

page 10

번호	정답
101	hoop
102	numb
103	feeble
104	obsolete
105	replicate
106	stem from
107	adjust A around B
108	sarcastic
109	consist in
110	intact
111	renown
112	absently
113	intoxicate
114	follow through on
115	overthrow
116	get to do
117	hereby
118	back out
119	shabby
120	absolve

Day 3

page 12

번호	정답
121	v. 녹이다; 종료시키다, 없어지다, 소실되다
122	a. 성숙한, 신중한
123	a. 빽빽한, 밀집한, 짙은
124	v. 베끼다, 필기하다
125	n. 살인
126	a. 잡기에 적합한; 이해력이 있는
127	v. 조롱하다, 경멸하다; n. 조롱, 경멸
128	v. 확신시키다, 보장하다
129	n. 양자 물리학
130	v. 취소하다, 철회하다
131	p. 왔던 길로 되돌아가다
132	p. 지나가는 말로
133	v. 따라잡다, 앞지르다
134	a. 이질적인
135	n. 녹 v. 녹슬다, 부식하다
136	v. 싸우다, 언쟁을 벌이다; 말다툼, 불만
137	a. 몹시 추운, 냉담한
138	p. 바르게 행동하다, 행동을 삼가다
139	a. 치명적인; 결정적인, 중대한
140	v. 대조확인하다, 입증하다, 증명하다, 검증하다

page 13

번호	정답
141	designate
142	placid
143	gourmet
144	eject
145	at all times
146	tuition
147	console
148	at all costs
149	be up for
150	sacred
151	eradicate
152	mimic
153	occupy
154	shed light on
155	jolt
156	terrain
157	come down with
158	fundamental
159	sufficient
160	disdain

page 14

번호	정답
161	have a good head on one's shoulders
162	fraction
163	tidy
164	ruin
165	devise
166	discourse
167	distress
168	impulse
169	eloquent
170	polarity
171	poignant
172	incorporate
173	folklore
174	costly
175	disparity
176	shatter
177	homage
178	nasty
179	affair
180	deflect

Day 4

page 16

번호	정답
181	v. 사임하다
182	v. 흐느껴 울다
183	n. 박차, 자극 v. 원동력이 되다
184	a. 무례한, 버릇없는
185	v. 멸망하다, 갑자기 죽다; 썩다; 타락하다
186	v. 관련시키다; 교제하다 n. 동료, 친구
187	p. ~에 참여하다; ~로 받아들이다
188	p. ~중에 많이, 더, 더 많이
189	a. 이성애의
190	p. A를 B에 집중시키다
191	v. 조직화하다, 조정하다
192	n. (남성용) 바지
193	a. 고독한, 혼자의
194	p. A를 B와 관련시키다
195	a. 효과적으로 보여 주는; 효과적인, 효험이 있는
196	n. 관; 시체를 담는 상자
197	n. 짧음; 간결
198	n. 주행기록장치
199	p. ~을 시작하다; 방법을 찾다
200	p. 기꺼이 ~하다

page 17

번호	정답
201	mischance
202	litigate
203	speculate
204	superfluous
205	bosom
206	pauper
207	misplace
208	as we speak
209	induce
210	out of date
211	make at
212	reminiscent
213	mobilize
214	in favor with
215	plumber
216	requisite
217	have a taste for
218	dormant
219	admiral
220	get a handle on

page 18

번호	정답
221	barn
222	make allowance for
223	temperate
224	distort
225	verdict
226	mortal
227	disjoint
228	ask after
229	at a glance
230	at the best
231	infection
232	fling
233	thermal
234	diffuse
235	wavelength
236	annuity
237	scrutinize
238	collect on
239	carry away
240	compass

Day 5

page 20

번호	정답
241	n. 열광자, 광신자
242	p. 효력이 발생하다
243	v. (불을 붙이다), 태우다
244	p. ~에서 자신의 몫을 다하다
245	v. 오래 머무르다; 지속되다
246	p. 인도하다, 넘기다
247	n. 취임, 계승; 동의; 부가, 부가물
248	a. 제멋대로인, 변덕스러운
249	n. 본질, 실체; 물질
250	p. 서로
251	v. 좌절감을 주다; 방해하다
252	n. 비굴한 태도 v. 굽실대다
253	n. 명성, 위신
254	v. 모이다, 집합시키다
255	v. 할당하다, 배당하다
256	v. 결정하다, 측정하다, 판정하다
257	p. ~에서 물려받다
258	n. 무리; 송이; 성단; v. 밀집시키다
259	p. ~에 반응하다
260	v. 존경하다

page 21

번호	정답
261	eligible
262	one after another
263	wipe out
264	be absorbed in
265	roam
266	line of attack
267	opposed to N
268	let alone
269	cultivate
270	interlock
271	accuse
272	gymnasium
273	credulous
274	all at once
275	pioneer
276	compassion
277	reprehend
278	jump to a conclusion
279	grant
280	array

page 22

번호	정답
281	debate
282	revalidate
283	make a commotion
284	priest
285	gorgeous
286	indicate
287	in this regard
288	nausea
289	cohabit
290	quotation
291	by usage
292	injure
293	collapse
294	make A a regular habit
295	vigor
296	entreat
297	fate
298	manipulate
299	bygone
300	disturb

Day 6

page 24

번호	정답
301	n. 정반대, 대립; 대조
302	v. 비방하다, 중상하다
303	n. 생리학, 생리 (기능)
304	a. 젊은
305	n. 애원, 간청, 답변
306	a. 위태로운, 위험한, 비판적인; 중요한
307	a. 강렬한, 치열한, 심한
308	n. 적, 원수
309	n. 경솔, 변덕, 경솔한 행위
310	n. 실질적인 것, 진짜
311	n. 분화구
312	a. 제 때가 아닌; 너무 이른
313	n. 약체, 약자
314	n. 멈춤, 중단 v. 멈추다, 서다
315	n. 슬픔, 비애, 후회: 불운, 재난
316	v. 나아가다, 행진하다 n. 3월
317	p. ~의 본보기가 되다
318	n. 정권, 제도, 체제
319	a. 제1의, 주요한, 최초의, 주된
320	v. 관통하다, 침투하다

page 25

번호	정답
321	be engrossed in
322	endeavor
323	proximity
324	impracticable
325	comprehensive
326	virtu
327	eliminate
328	tangible
329	in any case
330	acclaim
331	marvelous
332	falsehood
333	archaic
334	be exposed to
335	barley
336	ludicrous
337	take A further
338	trace
339	at most
340	profit

page 26

번호	정답
341	administration
342	eternal
343	set in one's way
344	qualified to do
345	a majority of
346	abstract
347	belong to N
348	mutation
349	adjudicate
350	embark
351	emerge
352	across the table
353	get off the ground
354	mortify
355	congress
356	adorn
357	blister
358	suffix
359	by heart
360	sabotage

Day 7

page 28

번호	정답
361	p. 제자리를 찾다, 아귀가 맞다
362	p. 전혀 ~이 아닌, ~와는 거리가 먼
363	p. ~에 기초하다
364	p. 담보로
365	v. 가치를 떨어뜨리다
366	v. 주지 않다, 받지 않다, 억제하다
367	adv. 아마
368	n. 육식동물
369	n. 나뭇가지; 지점, 지사
370	n.. 역경, 곤경 v. 맹세하다
371	p. 위에서, 위로부터
372	p. 아마 ~일 것이다
373	n. 지루함
374	n. 신경, 긴장, 불안
375	n. 불행, 고통, 비참(함)
376	n. 알갱이, 작은 입자
377	v. 완전히 파괴하다
378	p. ~를 좋아하다, ~를 찾다
379	a. 신중을 요하는, 민감한; 허약한; 맛있는
380	v. 점검하다; 따라잡다

page 29

번호	정답
381	fiery
382	connect with
383	fragile
384	outright
385	notwithstanding
386	at the expense of
387	give a hand
388	shrub
389	grievance
390	explicit
391	conscience
392	cling
393	premonitory
394	malefactor
395	contend
396	resentment
397	resolve
398	detective
399	for fear of
400	successive

page 30

번호	정답
401	aberrant
402	hold good
403	pendulum
404	adjacent
405	reinforce
406	numerous
407	thrust
408	engage
409	joint
410	insomnia
411	intuition
412	let on
413	outcast
414	come out ahead
415	hazard
416	precise
417	publicity
418	imprint
419	disquiet
420	deteriorate

Day 8

page 32

번호	정답
421	n. 대리인, 변호사
422	n. 겸손
423	p. 처음부터
424	p. 단지 ~에 지나지 않는, ~일 뿐인
425	n. 영양 부족, 영양 실조
426	p. 최종적으로, 마지막으로 한 번만 더
427	v. 조정하다, 중재하다
428	a. 정교한, 매우 아름다운
429	n. 복장
430	p. ~와 제휴하여, 협력하여
431	n. 급함, 서두름; v. 서두르다
432	n. 연회, 잔치, 축제일 v. 맘껏 먹다, 포식하다
433	v. 얼굴을 붉히다, 빨개지다
434	v. 의견이 일치하다
435	a. 불규칙의, 비정형의, 이례적인
436	a. 완고한; 다루기 힘든; 지우기 힘든
437	a. 거대한, 어마어마한, 엄청난
438	p. 적어도
439	n. 다른 생각 a. 이단의, 비전통의
440	a. 악명이 높은

page 33

번호	정답
441	in the abstract
442	after the fact
443	in proportion to
444	in harmony with
445	fabulous
446	clean out
447	amenity
448	hatch
449	suppress
450	manifest
451	gratitude
452	commodity
453	endear
454	pursue
455	torture
456	maze
457	endure
458	bring on
459	pulp
460	illuminate

page 34

번호	정답
461	extract
462	miscarry
463	monarchy
464	erect
465	one after the other
466	retina
467	ingrain
468	casualty
469	at the mercy of
470	crawl
471	the masses
472	ban
473	recourse
474	malfunction
475	compatible
476	call names
477	auxiliary
478	trivial
479	demand
480	disinterested

Day 9

page 36

번호	정답
481	v. 부유하게 하다, 풍요롭게 하다
482	v. 식별하다, 분별하다
483	a. 적합한, 적절한
484	a. 신랄한
485	v. 자극하다, 불을 붙이다, 타오르다
486	a. 거두절미한, 간결한
487	n. 떼, 무리; 떼 지어가다
488	p. ~에게 공격적인
489	p. 효과를 미치다
490	n. 담보물, 인질
491	a. 힘이 없는, 무기력한
492	a. 관대한, 개방적인; 자유주의의
493	a. 은밀한, 내밀한, 기밀의
494	n. 무리, 떼; 벌 떼 v. 무리를 지어 다니다
495	n. 포로 a. 사로잡힌, 억류된
496	v. 변성시키다, 성질을 바꾸다
497	v. 묵다, 체류하다
498	n. 균류, 곰팡이류; 균상종
499	p. 재화와 용역
500	v. 유리를 끼우다; 유약을 칠하다 n. 유약

page 37

번호	정답
501	keen
502	exact to the life
503	acquisitiveness
504	liable
505	ripe
506	at a loss
507	contrive
508	neutral
509	be obligated to do
510	embarrass
511	be fond of
512	appropriate
513	salute
514	at latest
515	procrastinate
516	celsius
517	transcend
518	depress
519	nasal
520	denounce

page 38

번호	정답
521	soothe
522	dazzle
523	distinguish
524	refer to N
525	posterity
526	discreet
527	resolute
528	gain access to
529	look back on
530	assume
531	public domain
532	pedagogy
533	affluent
534	despise
535	moderate
536	rule out
537	placate
538	discipline
539	hang up
540	startle

Day 10

page 40

번호	정답
541	n. 군중, 폭도, 떼
542	a. 자외선의
543	v. 확대하다, 강화하다, 증대시키다
544	p. 실제로, 사실은
545	a. 빽빽한; 간결한 n. 협정, 계약
546	a. 손쉬운, 수월한
547	v. 금지하다, 방해하다
548	v. 묵살하다, 간과하다
549	v. 섞이다, 어우러지다
550	v. 당황하게 하다, 실망하게 하다
551	v. 수혈하다
552	a. 사실에 입각한, 사실적인
553	a. 무모한, 신중하지 못한
554	v. 확언하다, 단언하다, 주장하다
555	p. ~에게 생각이 떠오르다
556	v. 던져넣다; 뛰어들다; 급락하다
557	v. 모으다, 모이다; 합계가 ~이 되다 n. 합계, 총액
558	v. 비방하다, 경시하다, ~을 얕보다
559	a. 촉각의
560	a. 사나운, 맹렬한

page 41

번호	정답
561	wear out
562	observe
563	ritual
564	bald
565	brute
566	as to
567	dominate
568	admonish
569	prognosis
570	conceit
571	take after
572	stroll
573	pin down
574	gracious
575	perceive
576	cabbage
577	interlude
578	swell
579	legislate
580	irrupt

page 42

번호	정답
581	have a handle on
582	word got around
583	undermine
584	go off
585	make one's way to
586	artery
587	adequate
588	enlist
589	rivulet
590	implement
591	geometry
592	disperse
593	autonomy
594	of service
595	peel
596	refuse
597	toss about
598	set out
599	distribute
600	indignant

Day 11

page 44

번호	정답
601	p. ~의 중심에
602	p. ~의 처분에 맡겨져
603	p. ~에 익숙해지다
604	n. 신조, 신념, 원칙; 교의
605	n. 변천, 전이
606	p. ~의 경우에는
607	a. 뒤얽힌, 복잡한
608	a. 강변의
609	a. 민족의, 종족의
610	n. 존경, 경의; 존경하다, 존중하다
611	v. 통역하다, 해석하다, 이해하다, 설명하다
612	n. 혜성
613	p. A를 B로 끌어들이다
614	n. 퇴비, 두엄 v. 퇴비를 만들다
615	n. 어원학
616	n. 악마, 악몽; 압박하는 일, 압박하는 사람
617	a. 기운이 없는, 다리를 절다, 절뚝거림
618	p. ~한 속도로
619	p. 그 반대를 보여 주는, 증명하는
620	n. 적대자, 반대자

page 45

번호	정답
621	heredity
622	demerit
623	alleviate
624	outdo
625	stain
626	statistics
627	deceive
628	draw a deep breath
629	restore
630	encyclopedia
631	inhale
632	desperado
633	parlor
634	deliberate
635	consistent with
636	anonymous
637	grow on
638	scant
639	audit
640	patron

page 46

번호	정답
641	vague
642	raid
643	compress
644	retrospect
645	superstition
646	account for
647	harry
648	by law
649	reduce
650	hit the books
651	clone
652	prominent
653	abhor
654	legitimate
655	go along with
656	brace
657	pardon
658	in a timely fashion
659	in the long run
660	anthropology

Day 12

page 48

번호	정답
661	p. 눈깜짝할 사이에
662	n. 놀라운 일 v. 놀라다
663	p. (찬찬히) 살펴보다, 점검하다; 재고 조사하다
664	a. 비이성적인, 무분별한
665	p. 결코 ~이 아닌
666	v. 구두점을 찍다, (말을) 중단시키다
667	v. 가로막다, 방해하다
668	p. 단결시키다
669	v. 일치하다, 조화되다 n. 합의
670	p. ~ 의 방법으로, ~에 의해서, ~을 거쳐서
671	a. 설치류의 n. 설치류 동물, 쥐
672	p. 단계적으로 도입하다
673	n. 위생
674	p. 뜻을 이해하다
675	v. 변동하다
676	v. 비난하다
677	v. 괴롭히다, 아프게 하다
678	n. 별표
679	n. 태아, 배
680	a. 전멸한, 멸종한

page 49

번호	정답
681	catastrophe
682	exalt
683	vintage
684	as far as it goes
685	dilute
686	pull out
687	disorder
688	natal
689	interface
690	come about
691	accurate
692	humble
693	divine
694	attain
695	hand-on
696	in view of
697	act as
698	with regard to
699	liken
700	deject

page 50

번호	정답
701	stalk
702	relic
703	deprive A of B
704	honour A with B
705	hold on
706	despond
707	tease
708	curb
709	fuss
710	detente
711	by now
712	multitude
713	on the surface
714	parallel
715	insofar as
716	get around
717	plumb
718	capitalize on
719	vine
720	consolidate

Day 13

page 52

번호	정답
721	n. 식초
722	n. 저장소, 저수지
723	v. 단념하다, 포기하다, 버리다
724	v. 평하다, 생각하다 n. 평판, 소문
725	v. 등록하다, 명부에 올리다, 가입하다
726	v. 억제하다, 진압하다
727	a. 습한, 습기가 있는
728	v. ~을 억누르다, 억제하다
729	v. 거르다, 선별하다
730	n. 상자
731	n. 성
732	p. 기어코, 어떠한 희생을 치르더라도
733	a. 신경의
734	n. 투표
735	p. ~하고 싶은, ~에 마음이 내켜서
736	v. 소홀히 하다, 경시하다; n. 태만, 경시
737	n. 믿음을 무너뜨리는 것, 반항
738	a. 뒤쪽; 뒤쪽의; 기르다, 양육하다
739	v. 모으다, 축적하다, 누적시키다, 점차 늘어나다
740	n. 보상(금)

page 53

번호	정답
741	at one's convenience
742	dissimulate
743	expend
744	repulse
745	by the same token
746	savage
747	discharge
748	severe
749	dwell
750	in consultation with
751	pedestal
752	mundane
753	deviate
754	meteor
755	transient
756	profound
757	tropic
758	inquire
759	struggle
760	connote

page 54

번호	정답
761	shelf-stable
762	adept
763	do A up
764	legacy
765	repeal
766	turn in
767	allege
768	as it were
769	primate
770	sustain
771	moron
772	amass
773	watchful
774	sit out
775	creep over
776	anguish
777	convince
778	factor in
779	grin
780	hostility

Day 14

page 56

번호	정답
781	p. 발달한 상태가 되다, 성년이 되다
782	n. 계급, 위계
783	v. 밀어내다, 쫓아내다
784	n. 저당물, 담보, 보증
785	a. 사춘기 청소년의, 청년의
786	p. 두드러지다, 눈에 띄다
787	n. (어떤 일에 소요되는) 기간
788	p. 대체로, 전체적으로 볼 때
789	p. A를 의심하다
790	a. 언어의, 언어학의
791	v. 잘못 말하다, 거짓 설명하다
792	n. (독단적인) 신조, 도그마
793	v. 고발하다
794	p. (고정핀으로) 뒤로 당겨서 묶다, 고정시키다
795	a. 무딘, 퉁명스러운
796	a. 편리한, 편의의
797	p. 승부에 지다
798	n. 왕좌, 왕위
799	a. 잔혹한, 잔인한
800	n. 비난, 책망 v. 비난하다

page 57

번호	정답
801	dislodge
802	antedate
803	component
804	with access to
805	somnambulism
806	renounce
807	abbreviate
808	county
809	dissonance
810	tyrant
811	accentuate
812	unearth
813	horticultural
814	standpoint
815	antinomy
816	sacrifice
817	diplomacy
818	invert
819	do away with
820	deadly

page 58

번호	정답
821	permit
822	deal with
823	embassy
824	reaction to N
825	elaborate
826	symmetry
827	comprehend
828	recollect
829	except for
830	constellation
831	stiff
832	dwell on
833	ambush
834	repel
835	by a hair's breadth
836	dissent
837	cite
838	downplay
839	commentary
840	a visit from the stork

Day 15

page 60

번호	정답
841	a. 가난한, 궁핍한, 필연적인
842	a. 지독한, 굉장히 무서운
843	n. 입장, 태도, 자세
844	a. 거장다운, 거장의
845	p. (특히 나쁜 영향을 받아) ~될 수 있는
846	n. 악인, 악한
847	n. 소요, 소동
848	v. 고정화하다, 굳어버리게 하다
849	v. 위태롭게 하다
850	n. 계획, 책략; v. 책략을 꾸미다
851	a. 호전적인
852	a. 과잉, 과잉의
853	v. 특허를 받다 n. 특허, 특허권
854	p. ~에 압박을 가하다
855	n. 뇌물 v. 뇌물을 주다; 매수하다
856	p. ~을 얻으려고 노력하다
857	p. 하고 싶은 대로, 내키는 대로
858	v. ~을 저장하다, 보존하다
859	v. 붕괴시키다, 분열시키다, 방해하다
860	n. 악의, 원한

page 61

번호	정답
861	clarify
862	flourish
863	subsidy
864	confer with
865	imply
866	naive
867	venture into
868	apparel
869	congestion
870	decay
871	deposit
872	impute
873	reed
874	allocate
875	stockpile
876	conduct
877	at home
878	relieve
879	courteous
880	bring A to a stop

page 62

번호	정답
881	archery
882	retort
883	live beyond one's income
884	outset
885	misuse
886	asthma
887	a bunch of
888	away from
889	pediatric
890	faculty
891	analogy
892	impose A on B
893	succor
894	oppress
895	come out
896	intrude
897	cross one's fingers
898	retrieve
899	go on errands
900	constitution

Day 16

page 64

번호	정답
901	v. (가구를) 비치하다, 제공하다
902	v. 줄어들다, 감소하다, 작아지다
903	n. 급정지; 장애 v. 매다, 연결하다; 얻어 타다
904	n. 기아, 기근; 결핍
905	v. 공모하다, 결탁하다
906	n. 초식동물
907	p. ~에 피해를 주는
908	v. 대피시키다, 철수시키다
909	p. ~을 잘게 자르다
910	n. (핵·세포 등의) 분열
911	p. 이를 위해, 그 목적을 달성하기 위하여
912	v. 불러 모으다, 소집하다
913	v. 조정하다, 화해시키다; 만족시키다
914	n. 사랑, 박애, 관용; 자선(행위), 자선(단체)
915	n. 감시, 감독, 관찰
916	n. 논평, 말 v. 논평하다, 발언하다, 주목하다
917	v. 거주하다, 살다
918	p. 통과되다, 성사되다, 해결하다
919	p. ~을 떠올리다, ~을 생각해 내다
920	v. 보내다, 전송하다; 전도하다; 전염시키다

page 65

번호	정답
921	conceive
922	prohibit
923	beloved
924	in one's opinion
925	abort
926	ferry
927	specimen
928	scent
929	mirage
930	all the same
931	lay off
932	subdue
933	doom
934	notable
935	feasible
936	intervene
937	luster
938	blow away
939	theology
940	confuse A with B

page 66

번호	정답
941	popularity
942	defeat
943	out of tune
944	at one time
945	on one hand
946	melancholy
947	column
948	come in handy
949	contaminate
950	half off
951	reveal
952	spank
953	solicit
954	superb
955	lure
956	confront
957	refuge
958	come on
959	calf
960	opposite to N

Day 17

page 68

번호	정답
961	a. 합성한, 인조의, 종합적인
962	n. 구멍; 충치
963	a. 근심 걱정 없는, 무관심한
964	n. 다신론, 다신교
965	p. ~를 줄이다
966	p. 해결하다; 다리미질하다
967	v. 응고하다; 단결하다; 확고해지다
968	a. 사려깊은, 현명한
969	n. 몰수, 장악; 발작, 경련
970	v. 공들여 만들다 n. 공예, 기술
971	n. 일치, 조화
972	v. 권력을 휘두르다
973	p. ~에 의하여, ~의 도움으로
974	v. 뒤얽히게 하다, 관련지우다, 꼬아 짜다
975	n. 헌사, 공물
976	v. 물러나다, 희미해지다, 약해지다
977	a. 간단한, 솔직한
978	v. 주관하다, 주재하다
979	v. 호기심을 불러일으키다; 모의하다 n. 음모
980	n. 여드름

page 69

번호	정답
981	reptile
982	protagonist
983	hit the ceiling
984	desecrate
985	approximate
986	be in the way
987	genuine
988	garment
989	abdicate
990	fortify
991	thread
992	faucal
993	green thumb
994	get on with
995	obscene
996	embellish
997	reign
998	trespass
999	barter
1000	stray

page 70

번호	정답
1001	refract
1002	bring about
1003	testify
1004	adjourn
1005	suffocate
1006	dissemble
1007	recession
1008	asperse
1009	extemporize
1010	have a point
1011	timely
1012	recess
1013	cold to N
1014	decade
1015	by a factor of
1016	vegetation
1017	what A like
1018	starve
1019	despair
1020	humanitarian

Day 18

page 72

번호	정답
1021	v. 밝히다, 명료하게 설명하다
1022	v. 다하다, 이행하다, 충족하다
1023	a. 말의, 문자 그대로의
1024	a. 또렷한, 명백한, 외견상의, 겉보기에는
1025	p. ~이라는 것을 고려하면
1026	a. 호화로운, 값비싼
1027	n. 해독, 소독
1028	v. 마비시키다, 활동 불능이 되게 하다
1029	p. ~와 동일하다
1030	v. 비난하다; 선고하다
1031	p. 좋아, 한 번 해봐
1032	n. 보행자; 평범한, 진부한
1033	p. 뜯어내다, 훔치다
1034	p. ~에 문제가 있다; ~에 반대하다
1035	v. 동면하다
1036	n. 유아
1037	n. 발생률, 빈도
1038	a. 투명한;솔직한; 명쾌한, 이해하기 쉬운
1039	n. 목장
1040	a. 먹기에 좋은

page 73

번호	정답
1041	ascend
1042	distend
1043	vital
1044	pension
1045	foster
1046	wield
1047	fetch
1048	around the clock
1049	come to do
1050	coward
1051	repent
1052	methodical
1053	dynamic
1054	leave a mark on
1055	intermit
1056	flatter
1057	meditate
1058	in the same way
1059	on the contrary
1060	ramp

page 74

번호	정답
1061	tempt
1062	armament
1063	prick
1064	transaction
1065	backdrop
1066	let out
1067	at an early age
1068	barren
1069	carry on
1070	elementary
1071	tolerate
1072	close call
1073	inhabit
1074	astound
1075	dubious
1076	free from
1077	erratic
1078	seduce
1079	a quantity of
1080	robust

Day 19

page 76

번호	정답
1081	p. 다음 해에
1082	v. 강요하다, ~하게 하다
1083	a. 극단적인 v. 밖으로 소리를 내다
1084	p. ~에 대한 헌신
1085	v. 알아보다, 식별하다; 인정하다
1086	a. ~을 조건으로 하는; 우연한
1087	v. 깨다, 갈라지다; (사건·암호 등을) 풀다
1088	n. 가르침, 원리, 주의, 학설
1089	v. ~을 제한하다, 금지하다, 한정하다
1090	a. 심미적, 미학적, 미적인
1091	v. 비롯되다, 유래하다; 끌어내다, 유도하다
1092	v. 시인하다, 인정하다; 입학을 허가하다
1093	p. ~을 두려워하다, ~을 경외하다
1094	v. 새 풍토에 길들이다
1095	v. (말을) 끼워 넣어 억지 주장하다
1096	a. 일관된, 통일성이 있는, 논리적인
1097	a. 중요한, 결정적인
1098	n. 연소, 산화, 불에 탐
1099	v. 물 속에 잠기다, 가라앉히다
1100	a. 외고집의, 심술궂은, 사악한

page 77

번호	정답
1101	jump the queue
1102	deluxe
1103	contribution
1104	have difficulty in -ing
1105	arithmetic
1106	under consideration
1107	be attached to
1108	univocal
1109	inherent
1110	be capable of
1111	in the air
1112	subside
1113	defer
1114	impersonal
1115	depending on
1116	adhere
1117	vengeful
1118	cope with
1119	assemble
1120	yield

page 78

번호	정답
1121	concourse
1122	devour
1123	abundant
1124	implore
1125	conduce
1126	mooch
1127	pervert
1128	desperate
1129	tumble
1130	be frightened of
1131	abuse
1132	avert
1133	extinguish
1134	exterminate
1135	decree
1136	feint
1137	fad
1138	take precaution
1139	protest
1140	malevolent

Day 20

page 80

번호	정답
1141	v. (노력·돈·시간 따위를) 들이다, 바치다
1142	p. 전례가 없는, 들어본 적 없는
1143	n. 목초지, 방목지, 초원
1144	v. 한탄하다, 비판하다
1145	p. ~와 상충하는 / 모순되는
1146	v. 가입하다, 제휴하다 n. 계열사, 자회사
1147	a. 타고난, 선천적인
1148	n. 돌풍, 센바람
1149	n. 폭행, 폭력; 격렬함
1150	n. 원근법; 경치; 관점, 시야
1151	n. 흡인기
1152	n. 고소 공포증
1153	v. 덧붙이다, 추가하다
1154	v. 질식하게 만들다, 덮어서 불을 끄다
1155	v. 괴롭히다
1156	a. 시끄러운
1157	p. ~을 감당하기에 너무한
1158	p. ~이 없을 때에, ~이 없어서
1159	n. 깨달음
1160	v. 파묻다, 매장하다

page 81

번호	정답
1161	possess
1162	calculate
1163	courtship
1164	fur
1165	confer
1166	delegate
1167	ensue
1168	tribe
1169	holocaust
1170	entrust
1171	odor
1172	on the tube
1173	utensil
1174	constable
1175	lyric
1176	at one's expense
1177	falter
1178	alternative
1179	authentic
1180	deficit

page 82

번호	정답
1181	hollow
1182	at first glance
1183	wholesome
1184	queer
1185	epidemic
1186	implicit
1187	orphan
1188	pregnant
1189	take over
1190	more often than not
1191	lumber
1192	calculus
1193	spontaneous
1194	dwarf
1195	constituency
1196	loop
1197	elusiveness
1198	conform
1199	plural
1200	relegate

Day 21

page 84

번호	정답
1201	n. 니스, 광택제 v. 니스를 바르다
1202	n. 마굿간; 매점; 가판대; 칸막이 벽, 칸
1203	n. 하수, 오물, 오수
1204	a. 기름진, 비옥한
1205	a. 특유의, 특이한
1206	a. 미친듯이 서두는, 제정신이 아닌
1207	p. 처음부터, 처음에
1208	n. 소매, 소맷자락
1209	p. ~을 이용하다
1210	a. 가장 깊은, 친밀한
1211	n. 문지기, 수위, 관리인
1212	p. 그만큼 더
1213	n. 선봉, 선두
1214	a. 외부로부터의, 비본질적인
1215	n. 천연두
1216	a. 어색한, 곤란한
1217	n. 투표권, 선거권
1218	v. 외치다, 큰 소리로 말하다
1219	v. 연설하다, 낭독하다; 비난하다
1220	v. 침식하다

page 85

번호	정답
1221	altitude
1222	abominate
1223	have no choice but to do
1224	audiovisual
1225	dignity
1226	consonant
1227	trump
1228	catholic
1229	frank
1230	haul
1231	parish
1232	composure
1233	verge
1234	collision
1235	ascribe
1236	suit
1237	abstain
1238	splendid
1239	drain
1240	rejoice

page 86

번호	정답
1241	catch hold of
1242	intangible
1243	induct
1244	illiterate
1245	cane
1246	prosper
1247	standfast
1248	blossom
1249	inflict
1250	rag
1251	inspect
1252	at fault
1253	meteorology
1254	advocate
1255	in one's interest
1256	perspiration
1257	stout
1258	dedicate
1259	amicable
1260	confute

Day 22

page 88

번호	정답
1261	a. 암울한, 음습한
1262	a. 결함없는, 완벽한
1263	n. 만장일치
1264	n. 연무, 실안개; 희부연 것 v. 연무로 뒤덮이다
1265	p. 어찌할 바를 몰라
1266	p. ~을 책임지다
1267	n. 웅덩이
1268	n. 잠, 수면 v. 잠자다
1269	a. 선형의, 선적인
1270	v. 차별하다, 구별하다
1271	v. 매료하다, 매혹시키다
1272	v. 추론하다; 암시하다
1273	p. 계약을 맺다
1274	v. 불만스럽게 하다, 불쾌하게 만들다
1275	n. 공산주의
1276	p. 순간적으로 주저하다
1277	p. 잇달아, 연이어
1278	n. 공자(유교의 창시자)
1279	p. 여느 때와 달리, 기분 전환으로
1280	v. 닮다, 비슷하다

page 89

번호	정답
1281	obvious
1282	surpass
1283	arise
1284	alliance
1285	stationary
1286	obsess
1287	devout
1288	gross
1289	contravene
1290	cease to do
1291	serve two ends
1292	carpenter
1293	demote
1294	a great deal of
1295	pollen
1296	agile
1297	come off
1298	in conclusion
1299	on the grounds of
1300	merge into

page 90

번호	정답
1301	potential
1302	appear to do
1303	afflict
1304	except to do
1305	sanitary
1306	portray
1307	come to terms with
1308	be pressed for
1309	warrant
1310	segment
1311	mutual
1312	drawback
1313	capacity
1314	district
1315	suboptimal
1316	obscure
1317	call after
1318	excuse oneself for
1319	deter
1320	well off

Day 23

page 92

번호	정답
1321	n. 시도, 노력 v. 시도하다
1322	n. 난파, 잔해물, 잔해
1323	p. 할인하여
1324	p. ~을 두려워[경외]하다
1325	v. 말뚝을 뽑다, 분리하다, 파견하다
1326	n. 기압계
1327	n. 이중극, 쌍극자
1328	a. 텅 빈 / n. 공간
1329	p. ~하기 위하여, ~을 겨냥하여
1330	v. 생략하다, 빠뜨리다
1331	a. 눈의, 시각의; 빛을 이용하는
1332	v. 임명하다, 공천하다
1333	n. 보도, 방송, 보급
1334	v. 약해지다, 시들해지다 n. 감소, 쇠퇴
1335	n. 맛, 즐거움 v. 즐기다
1336	v. 흩뿌리다; 점재시키다
1337	n. 반역자, 반항아 v. 반란을 일으키다
1338	p. A를 B로 대체하다
1339	n. 성명, 성명서; 명세서; 진술, 연설
1340	p. 오랫동안, 상세히

page 93

번호	정답
1341	hot under the collar
1342	outlandish
1343	utilitarianism
1344	ruddy
1345	catch up on
1346	at times
1347	outspoken
1348	inevitable
1349	disclaim
1350	cumulative
1351	oat
1352	fit in with
1353	state of the art
1354	make the point that
1355	make believe
1356	realty
1357	aviation
1358	radius
1359	remnant
1360	be scared of

page 94

번호	정답
1361	dispense
1362	ethics
1363	rub
1364	hold one's tongue
1365	inflow
1366	exotic
1367	banquet
1368	decent
1369	progeny
1370	contemn
1371	gloomy
1372	significant
1373	correlated with
1374	sheer
1375	grief
1376	admit to N
1377	ahead of
1378	query
1379	subtle
1380	shrink

Day 24

page 96

번호	정답
1381	n. 자두
1382	v. 당황하게 하다
1383	v. 속이다; 즐겁게 하다
1384	v. 해부하다, 분석하다
1385	p. ~하기 쉬운
1386	v. 악보로 표시하다; 기록하다, 적어두다
1387	v. 제압하다, 압도하다
1388	v. 포기하다, 양도하다, 단념하다
1389	a. 거만한, 오만한
1390	n. 풍미, 향미, 맛; 향미로, 조미료
1391	v. 연장하다
1392	v. 고집하다, 노력하다, 견디다
1393	a. 충분한
1394	v. 내뿜다, 방출하다
1395	p. A를 끌어내다
1396	v. 박수갈채하다; 칭찬하다
1397	v. 인정하다; 사례하다, 감사하다
1398	v. 시들다, 말라 죽다
1399	p. A에 맞춘 듯이 꼭 맞아떨어지다
1400	n. 규정, 조항, 공급, 대비

page 97

번호	정답
1401	creep
1402	tariff
1403	rap
1404	apparatus
1405	amnesia
1406	incense
1407	prove a point
1408	harsh
1409	lament
1410	impure
1411	irrespective
1412	go well with
1413	retract
1414	be down on
1415	curse
1416	obstruct
1417	aborigine
1418	to begin with
1419	gill
1420	psychiatric

page 98

번호	정답
1421	can afford to do
1422	cemetery
1423	mourn
1424	align
1425	of name
1426	equator
1427	pneumonia
1428	velocity
1429	to a person
1430	divert
1431	poise
1432	ignoble
1433	prefer A to B
1434	transgress
1435	abrasive
1436	spare
1437	no sooner A than B
1438	outweigh
1439	imperial
1440	move around

Day 25

page 100

번호	정답
1441	a. ~에 열중하고 있는
1442	n. 식민지; 집단, 부락, 군집, 군체
1443	n. 이슬
1444	p. 운동하다; 알아내다, 해결하다; 계산하다
1445	v. 짜증나게 하다; (피부 등을) 자극하다
1446	v. 비난하다, 질책하다
1447	p. ~에도 불구하고, ~에 직면하여
1448	p. 영양제를[알약을] 복용하다
1449	v. 수확하다
1450	n. 당뇨병
1451	v. 부식하다
1452	a. 어울리지 않는, 지나친, 과도한; 불법의, 부당하
1453	a. 원시의, 원시적인
1454	v. 암살하다
1455	v. 구체화 하다; 포함하다
1456	v. 껴안다, 받아들이다
1457	a. 울리는, 울려 퍼지는
1458	adv. 무심코, 분별없이, 어리석게
1459	n. (시계의) 추, 진자
1460	v. 조직하다; 오케스트라용으로 편곡하다

page 101

번호	정답
1461	alienation
1462	mast
1463	gaze
1464	turmoil
1465	conceal
1466	ware
1467	malaria
1468	lodge
1469	proceeds
1470	go up
1471	for this once
1472	irrigate
1473	constrict
1474	on one's own
1475	confederate
1476	duplicate
1477	paddle
1478	artifice
1479	vicious
1480	nexus

page 102

번호	정답
1481	marinate
1482	ambient
1483	persist in
1484	go with
1485	rise to the bait
1486	school supplies
1487	coincide with
1488	commend
1489	polish
1490	catch oneself
1491	in no way
1492	ethanol
1493	phenomenon
1494	indifferent
1495	make no mistake about
1496	accede
1497	refute
1498	get along with
1499	rash
1500	assimilate

Day 26

page 104

번호	정답
1501	n. 윤곽, 외형; 지형선, 등고선
1502	a. 수직의, 세로의
1503	n. 분쟁, 불화, 반목
1504	p. ~을 처리하다
1505	p. ~하려는 노력으로
1506	p. 더 자세히 살펴보면
1507	n. 불협화음
1508	n. 상인, 무역상
1509	v. ~한 상태로 만들다; 주다, 제공하다; 표현하다
1510	p. 막 ~하려 하다
1511	n. 가설
1512	p. ~에서 분리되다
1513	n. 위도; 허용범위
1514	v. 만기가 되다, 끝나다
1515	p. ~을 물려주다
1516	n. 무질서
1517	a. 공간의, 공간적인
1518	v. 대체하다, 바꾸다; 대신하다
1519	p. ~을 어려움에 빠뜨리다
1520	p. ~의 비용 부담으로

page 105

번호	정답
1521	crook
1522	exile
1523	profess
1524	antebellum
1525	insist
1526	compulsive
1527	look on
1528	abolish
1529	in the raw
1530	obedient
1531	feign
1532	cosmopolitan
1533	strain
1534	decipher
1535	cut off
1536	chronic
1537	cut out
1538	reciprocal
1539	presume
1540	scarcity

page 106

번호	정답
1541	track down
1542	evoke
1543	get A out
1544	advert
1545	take a measure
1546	denote
1547	pitfall
1548	vulnerable to N
1549	redeem
1550	fixate
1551	predator
1552	in any event
1553	at hand
1554	expel
1555	prompt
1556	disembodied
1557	all but
1558	fame
1559	urge
1560	pragmatic

Day 27

page 108

번호	정답
1561	p. ~의 비율로
1562	a. 만족해 하는, 자기 만족의
1563	conj. ~하지 않도록
1564	n. 자갈
1565	v. 수분을 제거하다, 건조시키다
1566	v. 구출시키다, 탈출시키다
1567	n. 배우자
1568	a. 최선의, 최적의
1569	p. ~와 토론을 벌이다
1570	p. 일어나다, 발생하다
1571	a. 독실한, 경건한
1572	v. 선언하다, 공표하다
1573	v. 귀화시키다
1574	p. A에게 B를 주다, 투자하다
1575	n. (약의 1회분) 복용량, 투여량
1576	p. 막다, 제지하다
1577	n. 피로(* 밭일로 피곤한)
1578	v. 소화하다; 이해하다
1579	p. 더 나쁠 거 없는, 똑같은
1580	n. 증강 v. 증강시키다

page 109

번호	정답
1581	at the beginning of
1582	on hold
1583	get A out of the way
1584	What with A and B
1585	lessen
1586	dialect
1587	adapt to N
1588	stagnant
1589	celerity
1590	serve to do
1591	exaggerate
1592	devastate
1593	mandatory
1594	sake
1595	smear
1596	while away
1597	absurd
1598	take up the issue
1599	affect
1600	transmittance

page 110

번호	정답
1601	against the laws
1602	racism
1603	at no cost
1604	diagonal
1605	quantum
1606	withdraw
1607	undertake
1608	terminate
1609	adjust to N
1610	imperative
1611	flesh
1612	neologism
1613	timorous
1614	solemn
1615	fury
1616	enchant
1617	surge
1618	nothing but
1619	adjoin
1620	take A into account

Day 28

page 112

번호	정답
1621	v. 시작하다, 착수하다; 전수하다
1622	v. (얼굴이) 붉어지다; 물이 쏟아지다
1623	p. ~하기만 하면 된다.
1624	p. 옳다고 믿으며, 선의로
1625	p. ~을 견디다
1626	v. 요약하다, 단축시키다
1627	a. 유능한, 능숙한
1628	a. 원인이 되는
1629	p. 깊숙이, 핵심까지
1630	v. 재발하다, 반복되다
1631	p. ~을 맡다
1632	p. 호랑이도 제 말하면 온다
1633	v. 헐떡거리다, 숨이 막히다
1634	n. 속기, 약칭 v. 속기하다
1635	p. 멍하게
1636	v. 환대, 후한 대접
1637	v. 방해하다
1638	n. 선례, 판례, 전례
1639	n. 고고학
1640	p. ~을 갖춘

page 113

번호	정답
1641	diminish
1642	reciprocate
1643	entail
1644	impoverish
1645	herd
1646	sort out
1647	committee
1648	taboo
1649	stake
1650	controversy
1651	in search of
1652	lunar
1653	parliament
1654	suspend
1655	missionary
1656	malign
1657	betray
1658	poverty
1659	sting
1660	break the news to

page 114

번호	정답
1661	indelicate
1662	outage
1663	inhibit
1664	be skilled in
1665	nurture
1666	get down to
1667	enter into
1668	petroleum
1669	revenue
1670	punctual
1671	scavenger
1672	swift
1673	not so much A as B
1674	forbear
1675	get the better of
1676	unease
1677	sneeze
1678	ablaze
1679	complicit
1680	predominant

Day 29

page 116

번호	정답
1681	p. ~하기만 하면
1682	v. 처형하다; 실행하다
1683	v. ~을 취소하다, 무효로 하다
1684	n. 농담, 조롱 v. 농담하다
1685	v. 인정하다, 시인하다; 고백하다
1686	v. 얻다, 획득하다
1687	p. 24시간 내내
1688	a. 인민주의의, 인민당의 n. 포퓰리스트, 인민주의자
1689	a. 토착의, 원주민의
1690	v. 영양분을 주다, 육성하다
1691	n. 현자
1692	a. 장엄한, 당당한
1693	n. 부업; 취미
1694	v. 손상시키다
1695	n. 이익, 원조, 자기편; 지지
1696	v. 압축하다; 액화되다, 고체화되다
1697	p. A를 버리다
1698	p. 글씨를 잘 쓰다
1699	n. 목초지, 초원
1700	p. ~을 우연히 발견하다

page 117

번호	정답
1701	awe
1702	desolate
1703	penitent
1704	proportion
1705	burglar
1706	at its highest
1707	descry
1708	endanger
1709	include out
1710	icing
1711	intrinsic
1712	confine
1713	subtract
1714	impromptu
1715	progency
1716	in contact with
1717	swallow
1718	allude
1719	succumb
1720	council

page 118

번호	정답
1721	appeal to N
1722	archive
1723	delegate A to B
1724	aptitude
1725	sedentary
1726	proponent
1727	aftermath
1728	tense
1729	abrupt
1730	undo
1731	convert
1732	contagious
1733	coincide
1734	back down
1735	mutually exclusive
1736	interfere
1737	fall on
1738	drudgery
1739	indulge
1740	subordinate

Day 30

page 120

번호	정답
1741	n. 기념품
1742	v. 다시 활기를 띠게 하다
1743	n. 멍, 타박상
1744	n. 인구 조사
1745	v. 명령으로 추방하다
1746	n. 추론, 연역; 공제, 공제액
1747	v. 성큼성큼 걷다, 활보하다; 큰 걸음, 보폭
1748	v. (옷을 차려) 입히다
1749	v. 예배하다, 숭배하다
1750	n. 소매, 소매상 a. 소매의, 소매상의
1751	a. 공감할 수 있는, 감정 이입의
1752	a. 인식의, 인지의
1753	p. A를 사형에 처하다
1754	p. 게다가, 더욱이
1755	v. 사라지다, 소멸하다
1756	p. 현상 유지
1757	p. ~을 넘어서다, ~을 지나가다
1758	v. 깡충 뛰다
1759	n. 속편, 후속
1760	v. 용서하다

page 121

번호	정답
1761	metabolic
1762	silhouette
1763	pathetic
1764	petty
1765	on one's feet
1766	intimidate
1767	oath
1768	contribute to N
1769	control over
1770	pessimist
1771	distract
1772	beware
1773	tin
1774	manufacture
1775	trepid
1776	corridor
1777	lad
1778	annul
1779	anticipate
1780	sequence

page 122

번호	정답
1781	in the light of
1782	come across as
1783	make it a rule to do
1784	in a big way
1785	snuff
1786	reprove
1787	shiver
1788	cup of tea
1789	continence
1790	acquit
1791	keep up to date
1792	mislead
1793	fraud
1794	immune to N
1795	aggrieve
1796	utmost
1797	astonish
1798	dismiss
1799	ambiguous
1800	sow

Day 31

page 124

번호	정답
1801	n. 정상, 산꼭대기 a. 정상회담의
1802	v. 피하다, 벗어나다
1803	n. 우화, 비유담
1804	p. 쇠퇴하여, 기울어
1805	v. 코를 골다
1806	p. 차례로
1807	p. ~와 공통으로 / ~와 같게
1808	n. 사료, 으깬 음식 v. 으깨다
1809	v. 우연히 만나다
1810	n. 특권, 특전
1811	a. 통통한, 토실토실한
1812	n. 열망, 포부, 대망, 동경
1813	v. 고갈시키다, 소모시키다
1814	n. 상속인 , 후계자
1815	p. 그림을 그리다; ~에 의존하다
1816	v. 나아가게 하다, 추진하다
1817	n. 경도
1818	n. 선박; 혈관; 용기
1819	p. ~한 가격으로
1820	p. 결국 ~이 되다

page 125

번호	정답
1821	at peace
1822	longevity
1823	derange
1824	hold onto
1825	anecdote
1826	blame A on B
1827	release
1828	attribute
1829	inspire
1830	sew
1831	apathy
1832	untapped
1833	defect
1834	at the rate of
1835	interdict
1836	province
1837	criterion
1838	unassuming
1839	pupil
1840	run for

page 126

번호	정답
1841	moan
1842	underpin
1843	dispose of
1844	accomplish
1845	corpse
1846	be to blame for
1847	spine
1848	approve of
1849	no less than
1850	regress
1851	infrastructure
1852	allow for
1853	greed
1854	heritage
1855	compensate
1856	reverse
1857	abet
1858	slip away
1859	contradict
1860	con

Day 32

page 128

번호	정답
1861	p. ~과 일치하다, ~에 상응하다
1862	v. ~에게 명령하다; 금하다
1863	a. 수사적인, 미사여구식의, 과장이 심한
1864	a. 도덕적인
1865	a. 경향이 있는, ~하기 쉬운; 어드려 있는
1866	v. 퇴화하다, 퇴보하다, 타락하다
1867	v. 사귀다, 어울리다 n. 배우자
1868	v. 어리둥절하게 만들다
1869	n. 창자, 장 a. 본능적인, 근본적인
1870	v. 보다, 바라보다
1871	v. 보험에 들다
1872	a. 마실 수 있는
1873	n. 동료, 또래 친구
1874	n. 합성물, 합성어 v. 혼합하다, 합성하다
1875	p. 탄소 발자국
1876	a. 세련된, 경험 많은; 정교한, 복잡한
1877	a. 대담한
1878	a. 유효한
1879	p. 나누어지다, 분할되다
1880	a. 공평한, 편견 없는

page 129

번호	정답
1881	poke one's nose into
1882	complicate
1883	jurisdiction
1884	dispatch
1885	act against one's will
1886	glide
1887	carry weight
1888	incursion
1889	short of breath
1890	obesity
1891	breast
1892	terrific
1893	weird
1894	caught in
1895	murmur
1896	in the way
1897	medieval
1898	faint
1899	junction
1900	take A for granted

page 130

번호	정답
1901	guile
1902	be done with
1903	adverse
1904	affront
1905	rooted in
1906	consecutive
1907	ask a favor of
1908	fall away
1909	halve
1910	on exhibit
1911	conversant
1912	at the moment
1913	minister
1914	algebra
1915	hum
1916	monastery
1917	specimen
1918	conspire
1919	couple A with B
1920	have a breakdown

Day 33

page 132

번호	정답
1921	n. 치우친 사랑, 편애
1922	a. 비행의, 태만한; 체납된, 연체된, 미불의
1923	n. 상원 의원
1924	a. 재치있는
1925	p. ~에 익숙하다, ~을 잘 알다
1926	v. 기절시키다, 망연자실하게 만들다
1927	a. 싫어하는
1928	p. 애쓰다
1929	a. 엄청난, 막대한; 멋진
1930	p. A다 B라기 보다는
1931	v. ~와 일치하다
1932	v. 흡수하다, 받아들이다
1933	p. 기초 공사를 하다, 기초를 놓다
1934	v. 이해하다, 염려하다; 체포하다
1935	n. 처녀, 성모 a. 순수한
1936	n. 원정, 탐험
1937	a. 비극적인
1938	n. 순록
1939	v. 굴욕감을 주다, 자존심을 상하게 하다
1940	v. 잠기게 하다, 담그다; 몰두시키다

page 133

번호	정답
1941	commence
1942	break in
1943	insulate
1944	steer
1945	yearn
1946	paradox
1947	agony
1948	contemplate
1949	stand to do
1950	in the interests of
1951	shred
1952	voyage
1953	owe A to B
1954	be subjected to N
1955	trim
1956	monetary
1957	at a distance
1958	pensive
1959	backfire
1960	segregation

page 134

번호	정답
1961	feed on
1962	comply
1963	take leave
1964	corrupt
1965	deed
1966	omnibus
1967	breed
1968	indebt
1969	what with one thing and another
1970	little short of
1971	be aimed at
1972	benumb
1973	dispute
1974	bastard
1975	atmosphere
1976	take pride in
1977	of necessity
1978	impregnate
1979	perpetual
1980	converge

Day 34

page 136

번호	정답
1981	p. A와 B를 통합시키다
1982	v. 단언하다, 공언하다
1983	v. 유죄를 선고하다 n. 죄수
1984	a. 확실한, 확고한, 분명한
1985	v. 묘사하다, 서술하다
1986	n. 이타주의, 이타심
1987	a. 독점적인, 전용의, 배타적인
1988	p. 취소하다, 중지하다
1989	prep. 가운데에, ~으로 에워싸인
1990	p. 인기가 있다, 평판이 좋다
1991	p. ~에게 승리하다
1992	a. 숙달된, 능숙한
1993	n. 절약, 검약
1994	p. ~에 따라 행동하다; 조치를 취하다
1995	p. 한마디로
1996	v. 반대하다; 견디다, 참다, 저항하다
1997	a. 매우 귀중한
1998	p. 몸매를 가꾸다
1999	n. 만, 격차
2000	v. 침해하다, 가로채다

이그잼보카 고등 2000 4월

발 행 | 2024년 3월 4일
저 자 | 김동원
펴낸이 | 한건희
펴낸곳 | 주식회사 부크크
출판사등록 | 2014.07.15(제2014-16호)
주 소 | 서울특별시 금천구 가산디지털1로 110 SK트윈타워 A동 305호
전 화 | 1670-8316
이메일 | info@bookk.co.kr

ISBN | 979-11-410-7476-0

www.bookk.co.kr